KT-510-727

ONE HUNDRED FAVOURITE

LOVE POEMS

First published in the United Kingdom in 2002 by
Frith Book Company Ltd

Text and Design copyright © Frith Book Company Ltd
Photographs copyright © The Francis Frith Collection

The Frith photographs and the Frith logo are reproduced under licence from Heritage Photographic Resources Ltd, the owners of the Frith archive and trademarks

All rights reserved. No photograph in this publication may be sold to a third party other than in the original form of this publication, or framed for sale to a third party. No parts of this publication may be reproduced, stored in a retrieval system, or transmitted, in any form, or by any means, electronic, mechanical, photocopying, recording or otherwise, without the prior permission of the publishers and copyright holder.

British Library Cataloguing in Publication Data
One Hundred Favourite Love Poems
ISBN 1-85937-541-3

Frith Book Company Ltd
Frith's Barn, Teffont,
Salisbury, Wiltshire SP3 5QP
Tel: +44 (0) 1722 716 376
Email: info@francisfrith.co.uk
www.francisfrith.co.uk

Printed and bound in Spain

CONTENTS

1 *She was a Phantom of Delight*

SHE was a phantom of delight
When first she gleam'd upon my sight:
A lovely apparition, sent
To be a moment's ornament;
Her eyes as stars of Twilight fair;
Like Twilight's, too, her dusky hair;
But all things else about her drawn
From May-time and the cheerful dawn;
A dancing shape, an image gay,
To haunt, to startle, and waylay.

I saw her upon nearer view
A spirit, yet a woman too!
Her household motions light and free,
And steps of virgin-liberty;
A countenance in which did meet
Sweet records, promises as sweet;
A creature not too bright or good
For human nature's daily food,
For transient sorrows, simple wiles,
Praise, blame, love, kisses, tears, and smiles.

And now I see with eye serene
The very pulse of the machine;
A being breathing thoughtful breath,
A traveller between life and death:
The reason firm, the temperate will,
Endurance, foresight, strength, and skill;
A perfect woman, nobly plann'd
To warn, to comfort, and command;
And yet a Spirit still, and bright
With something of angelic light.

WILLIAM WORDSWORTH (1770-1850)

2 *The Secret*

I LOVED thee, though I told thee not,
Right earlily and long,
Thou wert my joy in every spot,
My theme in every song.
And when I saw a stranger face
Where beauty held the claim,
I gave it like a secret grace
The being of thy name.
And all the charms of face or voice
Which I in others see
Are but the recollected choice
Of what I felt for thee.

JOHN CLARE (1793-1864)

3 *To a Stranger*

PASSING stranger! you do not know
How longingly I look upon you,
You must be he I was seeking,
Or she I was seeking
(It comes to me as a dream)
I have somewhere surely
Lived a life of joy with you,
All is recall'd as we flit by each other,
Fluid, affectionate, chaste, matured,
You grew up with me,
Were a boy with me or a girl with me,
I ate with you and slept with you, your body has become
not yours only nor left my body mine only,
You give me the pleasure of your eyes,
face, flesh as we pass,
You take of my beard, breast, hands,
in return,
I am not to speak to you, I am to think of you
when I sit alone or wake at night, alone
I am to wait, I do not doubt I am to meet you again
I am to see to it that I do not lose you.

WALT WHITMAN (1819-1892)

4 *By Day Mine Eyes*

BY DAY mine eyes, by night my soul desires thee,
Weary, I lie alone.
Once in a dream it seemed thou wert beside me;
O far beyond all dreams, if thou wouldst come!

MS OF BEAUVAIS (9TH OR 10TH CENTURY)
TRANSLATED BY HELEN WADDELL

5 *Symptoms Of Love*

LOVE is a universal migraine,
A bright stain on the vision
Blotting out reason.

Symptoms of true love
Are leanness, jealousy,
Laggard dawns;

Are omens and nightmares—
Listening for a knock,
Waiting for a sign:

For a touch of her fingers
In a darkened room,
For a searching look.

Take courage, lover!
Can you endure such grief
At any hand but hers?

ROBERT GRAVES (1895-1985)

6 *Trust thou thy Love*

TRUST thou thy Love: if she be proud, is she not sweet?
Trust thou thy Love: if she be mute, is she not pure?
Lay thou thy soul full in her hands, low at her feet;
Fail, Sun and Breath!—yet, for thy peace, She shall endure.

JOHN RUSKIN (1819-1900)

7 *from La Vita Nuova: How Beatrice wakens Love*

IN HER eyes my lady bears Love,
by which she makes noble what she gazes on:
where she passes, all men turn their look on her,
and she makes the heart tremble in him she greets,
so that, all pale, he lowers his eyes,
and sighs, then, over all his failings:
anger and pride fleeing before her.
Help me, ladies, to do her honour!

All sweetness, all humble thought
are born in the heart of him who hears her speak,
and he who first saw her is blessed.

How she looks when she smiles a little,
can not be spoken of or held in mind,
she is so rare a miracle and gentle.

DANTE ALIGHIERI (1265-1321)
TRANSLATED BY A S KLINE

8 *from Maud*

COME into the garden, Maud,
For the black bat, night, has flown,
Come into the garden, Maud,
I am here at the gate alone;
And the woodbine spices are wafted abroad,
And the musk of the rose is blown.

For a breeze of morning moves,
And the planet of Love is on high,
Beginning to faint in the light that she loves
In a bed of daffodil sky,
To faint in the light of the sun she loves,
To faint in his light, and to die.

All night have the roses heard
The flute, violin, bassoon;
All night has the casement jessamine stirr'd
To the dancers dancing in tune;
Till a silence fell with the waking bird,
And a hush with the setting moon …

ALFRED, LORD TENNYSON (1809-1892)

9 *Odes Book 1, No 23*

CHLOE, you will not venture near,
Just like a lost young mountain deer
Seeking her frantic dam; for her each
Gust in the trees is a needless fear.

Whether the spring-announcing breeze
Shudders the light leaves or she sees
The brambles twitched by a green lizard,
Panic sets racing her heart and knees.

Am I a fierce Gaetulian
Lion or some tiger with a plan
To seize and maul you? Come, now, leave your
Mother: you're ready to know a man.

HORACE (65BC-8BC)
TRANSLATED JAMES MICHIE

10 *from Come, Sweetheart, Come*

COME, sweetheart, come,
  Dear as my heart to me,
Come to the room
  I have made fine for thee.

Here there be couches spread,
  Tapestry tented,
Flowers for thee to tread,
  Green herbs sweet scented.

Here is the table spread
  Love, to invite thee,
Clear is the wine and red,
  Love, to delight thee.

Sweet sounds the viol,
  Shriller the flute,
A lad and a maiden
  Sing to the lute ...

Dearest, delay not,
  Ours love to learn,
I live not without thee,
  Love's hour is come ...

MSS OF SALZBURG, CANTERBURY, AND LIMOGES 10TH CENTURY
TRANSLATED BY HELEN WADDELL

11 *from The Princess*

NOW sleeps the crimson petal, now the white;
Nor waves the cypress in the palace walk;
Nor winks the gold fin in the porphyry font:
The firefly wakens: waken thou with me.

Now droops the milkwhite peacock like a ghost,
And like a ghost she glimmers on to me.

Now lies the Earth all Danae to the stars,
And all thy heart lies open unto me.

Now slides the silent meteor on, and leaves
A shining furrow, as thy thoughts in me.

Now folds the lily all her sweetness up,
And slips into the bosom of the lake:
So fold thyself, my dearest, thou, and slip
Into my bosom and be lost in me.

ALFRED, LORD TENNYSON (1809-1892)

12 *from The Song of Solomon*

… I AM the rose of Sharon,
and the lily of the valleys.
As the lily among thorns,
so is my love among the daughters.
As the apple tree among the trees of the wood,
so is my beloved among the sons.

I sat down under his shadow with great delight,
and his fruit was sweet to my taste.
He brought me into the banqueting house,
and his banner over me was love.
Stay me with flagons, comfort me with apples:
for I am sick of love.

His left hand is under my head,
and his right hand doth embrace me.
I charge you, O ye daughters of Jerusalem,
by the roes, and by the hinds of the field,
that ye stir not up, nor awake my love,
till he please …

THE HOLY BIBLE

13 *There is no Loving after Death*

WHY hoard your maidenhood? There'll not be found
A lad to love you, girl, under the ground.
Love's joys are for the quick; but when we're dead
It's dust and ashes, girl, will go to bed.

ASCLEPIADES (FLORUIT 290BC)
TRANSLATED R A FURNESS

14 *from Twelfth Night*

O MISTRESS mine! Where are you roaming?
O! stay and hear; your true-love's coming,
That can sing both high and low.
Trip no further, pretty sweeting;
Journeys end in lovers meeting.
Every wise man's son doth know.

What is love? 'Tis not hereafter;
Present mirth hath present laughter;
What's to come is still unsure;
In delay there lies no plenty;
Then come kiss me, sweet and twenty!
Youth's a stuff will not endure.

WILLIAM SHAKESPEARE (1564-1616)

15 *from The Passionate Shepherd to His Love*

COME live with me and be my love,
And we will all the pleasures prove
That hills and valleys, dale and field,
And all the craggy mountains yield.

And we will sit upon the rocks,
And see the shepherds feed their flocks,
By shallow rivers to whose falls
Melodious birds sing madrigals.

There will I make thee beds of roses
And a thousand fragrant posies,
A cap of flowers, and a kirtle
Embroidered all with leaves of myrtle.

A gown made of the finest wool,
Which from our pretty lambs we pull,
Fair lined slippers for the cold,
With buckles of the purest gold …

The shepherds' swains shall dance and sing
For thy delight each May-morning:
If these delights thy mind may move,
Then live with me and be my love.

CHRISTOPHER MARLOWE (1564-1593)

16 *Love Song*

MY LOVE, we will go, we will go, I and you,
And away in the woods we will scatter the dew;
And the salmon behold, and the ousel too,
My love, we will hear, I and you, we will hear,
The calling afar of the doe and the deer.
And the bird in the branches will cry for us clear,
And the cuckoo unseen in his festival mood;
And death, oh my fair one, will never come near
In the bosom afar of the fragrant wood.

W B YEATS (1865-1939)

17 *from As You Like It*

IT WAS a lover and his lass,
  With a hey and a ho, and a hey-nonino!
That o'er the green cornfield did pass
  In the spring-time, the only pretty ring time,
When birds do sing, hey ding a ding ding:
Sweet lovers love the Spring.

Between the acres of the rye
  With a hey and a ho, and a hey-nonino,
These pretty country folks would lie:
  In the spring time, the only pretty ring time,
When birds do sing, hey ding a ding ding:
Sweet lovers love the Spring ...

And therefore take the present time,
  With a hey and a ho, and a hey-nonino!
For love is crowned with the prime,
  In the spring time, the only pretty ring time,
When birds do sing, hey ding a ding:
Sweet lovers love the Spring.

WILLIAM SHAKESPEARE (1564-1616)

18 *Love in Spring*

NOW the violet blooms again;
Blooms the lover of the rain,
The jonquil; blooms on every hill
The upland-roaming daffodil.
And now the favourite flower of Love,
Flower of spring, all flowers above,
In bloom perfected sweetly blows—
Zenophile, Persuasion's rose.
Meadows of your tresses fain,
You brightly laugh, but laugh in vain;
How sweet soe'er your posies be,
Far more excellent is she.

MELEAGER (FLORUIT 90BC)
TRANSLATED BY R A FURNESS

19 *from A Bean Field in Blossom*

MY LOVE is as sweet as a bean field in blossom;
Like the peabloom her cheek, like the dogrose her bosom:
My love, she's as rich as brook banks of daisies,
Gold eyes and silver rims meeting men's praises;
Her eyes are as bright as the brook's silver ripples,
Milk white are her twin breasts and rose pink the nipples;
Her ankles are sweet as a man can conceive,
And her arms are as fine too though hid in her sleeve ...

My love is as sweet as a bean field in blossom;
The snowdrop's not whiter than is her soft bosom:
The plash of the brook it is nothing so bright
As the beams of her eye by bonny moonlight:
The rose o' her cheek no garden so fair
Can match with the red carnations there:
We met where the beanfields were misted wi' dew,
And if she had kissed me why nobody knew.

JOHN CLARE (1793-1864)

20 *from Sonnets from the Portuguese*

IF THOU must love me, let it be for nought
    Except for love's sake only. Do not say,
    'I love her for her smile—her look—her way
Of speaking gently,—for a trick of thought
That falls in well with mine, and certes brought
    A sense of pleasant ease on such a day'—
    For these things in themselves, Beloved, may
Be changed, or change for thee—and love, so wrought,
May be unwrought so. Neither love me for
    Thine own dear pity's wiping my cheeks dry,—
A creature might forget to weep, who bore
    Thy comfort long, and lose thy love thereby!
But love me for love's sake, that evermore
    Thou mayst love on, through love's eternity.

ELIZABETH BARRETT BROWNING (1806-1861)

21 *Sonnet 18*

SHALL I compare thee to a summer's day?
Thou art more lovely and more temperate:
Rough winds do shake the darling buds of May,
And summer's lease hath all too short a date:

Sometime too hot the eye of heaven shines,
And often is his gold complexion dimm'd:
And every fair from fair sometime declines,
By chance, or nature's changing course, untrimm'd.

But thy eternal summer shall not fade
Nor lose possession of that fair thou ow'st;
Nor shall Death brag thou wander'st in his shade,
When in eternal lines to time thou grow'st:

So long as men can breathe, or eyes can see,
So long lives this, and this gives life to thee.

WILLIAM SHAKESPEARE (1564-1616)

22 *from Her Triumph*

… HAVE you seene but a bright Lillie grow
  Before rude hands have touch'd it?
Ha' you mark'd but the fall o' Snow
  Before the soyle hath smutch'd it?
Ha' you felt the wooll of the Beaver,
    Or Swan's Downe ever?
Or have smelt o' the bud o' the Brier,
    Or the Nard in the fire?
Or have tasted the bag of the Bee?
O so white! O so soft! O so sweet is she!

BEN JONSON (?1573-1637)

23 *O my Luve's Like a Red, Red Rose*

O MY Luve's like a red, red rose
  That's newly sprung in June:
O my Luve's like the melodie
  That's sweetly play'd in tune.

As fair thou art, my bonnie lass,
  So deep in luve am I:
And I will luve thee still, my dear,
  Till a' the seas gang dry:

Till a' the seas gang dry, my dear,
  And the rocks melt wi' the sun;
I will luve thee still, my dear,
  While the sands of life shall run.

And fare thee weel, my only Luve!
  And fare thee weel a while!
And I will come again, my Luve,
  Tho' it were ten thousand mile.

ROBERT BURNS (1759-1796)

24 *O Star of Mine*

THOU gazest on the stars:
  Would I might be,
O star of mine, the skies
With myriad eyes
  To gaze on thee.

PLATO (429BC-347BC)
TRANSLATOR UNKNOWN

25 *She Walks In Beauty*

SHE walks in beauty, like the night
   Of cloudless climes and starry skies,
And all that's best of dark and bright
   Meet in her aspect and her eyes,
Thus mellow'd to that tender light
   Which heaven to gaudy day denies.

One shade the more, one ray the less,
   Had half impair'd the nameless grace
Which waves in every raven tress,
   Or softly lightens o'er her face,
Where thoughts serenely sweet express
   How pure, how dear their dwelling-place.

And on that cheek and o'er that brow
   So soft, so calm, yet eloquent,
The smiles that win, the tints that glow
   But tell of days in goodness spent,
A mind at peace with all below,
   A heart whose love is innocent.

GEORGE GORDON, LORD BYRON (1788-1824)

26 *There Be None Of Beauty's Daughters*

THERE be none of Beauty's daughters
  With a magic like thee;
And like music on the waters
  Is thy sweet voice to me:
When, as if its sound were causing
The charmèd ocean's pausing,
The waves lie still and gleaming,
And the lull'd winds seem dreaming:

And the midnight moon is weaving
  Her bright chain o'er the deep,
Whose breast is gently heaving
  As an infant's asleep:
So the spirit bows before thee
To listen and adore thee;
With a full but soft emotion,
Like the swell of Summer's ocean.

GEORGE GORDON, LORD BYRON (1788-1824)

27 *Young and Gold-Haired*

YOUNG and gold haired, fair of face,
  Thou gav'st me tender kisses in my sleep.
If waking I may never look upon thee,
  O Sleep, I pray you, never let me wake!

MS OF ST REMY AT RHEIMS (9TH CENTURY)
TRANSLATED BY HELEN WADDELL

28 *from Beautiful Dreamer*

BEAUTIFUL Dreamer, wake unto me,
Starlight and dewdrops are waiting for thee;
Sounds of the rude world heard in the day,
Lulled by the moonlight have all passed away.

Beautiful dreamer, queen of my song
List while I woo thee with soft melody;
Gone are the cares of life's busy throng,
Beautiful dreamer awake unto me!
Beautiful dreamer awake unto me!

Beautiful dreamer, out on the sea,
Mermaids are chaunting the wild lorelei;
Over the streamlet vapours are borne,
Waiting to fade at the bright coming morn.
Beautiful dreamer, awake unto me!
Beautiful dreamer, wake unto me! ...

STEPHEN FOSTER (1826-1864)

29 *Life and Love*

LIFE, my Lesbia, life and love for ever!
All that gossip of grave and reverend elders—
close your ears to it! It's not worth a penny.
Suns can sink and return again next morning:
our brief day, when it once has been extinguished,
must pass into a sleep that has no waking.
Give me kisses—a thousand, then a hundred,
one more thousand and then another hundred,
then one thousand again, and still a hundred.
After that, when we've run up many thousands,
let's destroy the accounting and forget it,
so no envious character can hurt us
when he hears we have had so many kisses.

CATULLUS (c84BC-c54BC)
TRANSLATED BY GILBERT HIGHET

30 *Song to Celia*

DRINKE to me, onely with thine eyes,
  And I will pledge with mine;
Or leave a kisse but in the cup,
  And I'll not looke for wine.
The thirst, that from the soule doth rise,
  Doth aske a drinke divine:
But might I of Jove's Nectar sup,
  I would not change for thine.
I sent thee, late, a rosie wreath,
  Not so much honouring thee,
As giving it a hope, that there
  It could not withered bee.
But thou thereon did'st onely breath,
  And sent'st it backe to mee:
Since when it growes, and smells, I sweare,
  Not of it selfe, but thee.

BEN JONSON (?1573-1637)

31 *from Under The Balcony*

O BEAUTIFUL star with the crimson mouth!
  O moon with the brows of gold!
Rise up, rise up, from the odorous south!
    And light for my love her way,
    Lest her little feet should stray
  On the windy hill and the wold!
O beautiful star with the crimson mouth!
O moon with the brows of gold! …

O rapturous bird with the low, sweet note!
  O bird that sits on the spray!
Sing on, sing on, from your soft brown throat!
    And my love in her little bed
    Will listen, and lift her head
  From the pillow, and come my way!
O rapturous bird with the low, sweet note!
O bird that sits on the spray!

O blossom that hangs in the tremulous air!
  O blossom with lips of snow!
Come down, come down, for my love to wear!
    You will die on her head in a crown,
    You will die in a fold of her gown,
  To her little light heart you will go!
O blossom that hangs in the tremulous air!
O blossom with lips of snow!

OSCAR WILDE (1854-1900)

32 *from Romeo and Juliet*

BUT, soft! what light through yonder window breaks?
It is the east, and Juliet is the sun.
Arise, fair sun, and kill the envious moon,
Who is already sick and pale with grief
That thou her maid art far more fair than she.
Be not her maid, since she is envious;
Her vestal livery is but sick and green,
And none but fools do wear it; cast it off.
It is my lady: O, it is my love!
O, that she knew she were!
She speaks, yet she says nothing: what of that?
Her eye discourses; I will answer it.
I am too bold, 'tis not to me she speaks;
Two of the fairest stars in all the heaven,
Having some business, do entreat her eyes
To twinkle in their spheres till they return ...
See, how she leans her cheek upon her hand!
O, that I were a glove upon that hand,
That I might touch that cheek!

WILLIAM SHAKESPEARE (1564-1616)

33 *from A Subaltern's Love Song*

MISS J. Hunter Dunn, Miss J. Hunter Dunn,
Furnish'd and burnish'd by Aldershot sun,
What strenuous singles we played after tea,
We in the tournament—you against me!

Love-thirty, love-forty, oh! weakness of joy,
The speed of a swallow, the grace of a boy,
With carefullest carelessness, gaily you won,
I am weak from your loveliness, Joan Hunter Dunn.

Miss Joan Hunter Dunn, Miss Joan Hunter Dunn,
How mad I am, sad I am, glad that you won,
The warm-handled racket is back in its press,
But my shock-headed victor, she loves me no less ...

By roads 'not adopted', by woodlanded ways,
She drove to the club in the late summer haze,
Into nine-o'clock Camberley, heavy with bells
And mushroomy, pine-woody, evergreen smells.

Miss Joan Hunter Dunn, Miss Joan Hunter Dunn,
I can hear from the car-park the dance has begun,
Oh! full Surrey twilight! importunate band!
Oh! strongly adorable tennis-girl's hand!

Around us are Rovers and Austins afar,
Above us the intimate roof of the car,
And here on my right is the girl of my choice,
With the tilt of her nose and the chime of her voice.

And the scent of her wrap, and the words never said,
And the ominous, ominous dancing ahead.
We sat in the car park till twenty to one
And now I'm engaged to Miss Joan Hunter Dunn.

SIR JOHN BETJEMAN (1906-1984)

34 *To a Bride*

BLEST beyond earth's bliss, with heaven I deem him
Blest, the man that in thy presence near thee
Face to face may sit, and while thou speakest,
Listening may hear thee,

And thy sweet-voiced laughter: —In my bosom
The rapt heart so troubleth, wildly stirred:
Let me see thee, but a glimpse—and straightway
Utterance of word

Fails me; no voice comes; my tongue is palsied;
Thrilling fire through all my flesh hath run;
Mine eyes cannot see, mine ears make dinning
Noises that stun;

The sweat streameth down,—my whole frame seized with
Shivering,—and wan paleness o'er me spread,
Greener than the grass; I seem with faintness
Almost as dead.

SAPPHO (FLORUIT 600BC)
TRANSLATED BY WALTER HEADLAM

35 *To Lesbia*

SURELY that man equals the gods in heaven—
if it be not blasphemy, he excels them—
he who sits and, constantly, in your presence,
        watches and hears you
laugh with sweetness such that my shaken senses
leave me helpless. Lesbia, at the moment
when I first caught sight of you, then my voice was
        struck into silence,
tongue benumbed, light delicate flame pervaded
every limb, loud inward alarms were ringing
through my ears, while suddenly both my eyes were
        Covered with darkness.

CATULLUS (c84BC-c54BC)
TRANSLATED BY GILBERT HIGHET (THIS POEM IS CATULLUS'S TRANSLATION INTO LATIN OF THE PREVIOUS ONE WRITTEN IN GREEK)

36 *from To His Coy Mistress*

HAD we but world enough, and time,
This coyness, lady, were no crime ...
    But at my back I always hear
Time's winged chariot hurrying near;
And yonder all before us lie
Deserts of vast eternity.
Thy beauty shall no more be found,
Nor, in thy marble vault, shall sound
My echoing song; then worms shall try
That long preserv'd virginity ...
    Now therefore, while the youthful hue
Sits on thy skin like morning dew,
And while thy willing soul transpires
At every pore with instant fires,
Now let us sport us while we may;
And now, like am'rous birds of prey,
Rather at once our time devour,
Than languish in his slow-chapp'd power.
Let us roll all our strength, and all
Our sweetness, up into one ball;
And tear our pleasures with rough strife
Thorough the iron gates of life.
Thus, though we cannot make our sun
Stand still, yet we will make him run.

ANDREW MARVELL (1621-1678)

37 *from By a Bank of Pinks and Lilies*

DO NOT ask me, charming Phillis,
Why I lead you here alone,
By this bank of pinks and lilies
And of roses newly blown.

'Tis not to behold the beauty
Of those flowers that crown the spring;
'Tis to—but I know my duty,
And dare never name the thing ...

What the sun does to those roses,
While the beams play sweetly in,
I would—but my fear opposes,
And I dare not name the thing ...

On this bank of pinks and lilies,
Might I speak what I would do;
I would with my lovely Phillis—
I would; I would—Ah! would *you*?

ANONYMOUS c1724

38 *My Love in Her Attire*

MY LOVE in her attire doth show her wit,
It doth so well become her:
For every season she hath dressings, fit,
For Winter, Spring, and Summer.
No beauty she doth miss
When all her robes are on:
But Beauty's self she is,
When all her robes are gone.

ANON (17TH CENTURY)

39 *from Amores: Corinna in the Afternoon*

IT WAS hot, and the noon hour had gone by:
I was relaxed, limbs spread in the midst of the bed.
One half of the window was open, the other closed:
the light was just as it often is in the woods,
it glimmered like Phoebus dying at twilight,
or when night goes, but day has still not risen.
Such a light as is offered to modest girls,
whose timid shyness hopes for a refuge.
Behold Corinna comes, hidden by her loose slip,
scattered hair covering her white throat—
like the famous Semiramis going to her bed,
one might say, or Lais loved by many men.
I pulled her slip away—not harming its thinness much;
yet she still struggled to be covered by that slip …
When she stood before my eyes, the clothing set aside,
there was never a flaw in all her body.
What shoulders, what arms, I saw and touched!
Breasts formed as if they were made for pressing!
How flat the belly beneath the slender waist!
What flanks, what form! What young thighs!
Why recall each aspect? I saw nothing lacking praise
and I hugged her naked body against mine.
Who doesn't know the story? Weary we both rested.
May such afternoons often come for me!

OVID (43BC-AD18) TRANSLATED BY A S KLINE

40 *from Salome*

I AM amorous of thy body, Iokanaan!
Thy body is white, like the lilies of a field
  that the mower hath never mowed.
Thy body is white like the snows that lie on the
mountains of Judæa, and come down into the valleys.
The roses in the garden of the Queen of Arabia
  are not so white as thy body.
Neither the roses of the garden of the Queen of Arabia,
  the garden of spices of the Queen of Arabia, nor the feet
  of the dawn when they light on the leaves, nor the
  breast of the moon when she lies on the breast of the sea …
There is nothing in the world so white as thy body.
  Suffer me to touch thy body.

OSCAR WILDE (1854-1900)

41 *Ask Me No More*

ASK me no more where Jove bestows,
When June is past, the fading rose;
For in your beauty's orient deep,
These flowers, as in their causes, sleep.

Ask me no more whither do stray
The golden atoms of the day;
For in pure love heaven did prepare
Those powders to enrich your hair.

Ask me no more whither doth haste
The nightingale when May is past;
For in your sweet dividing throat
She winters, and keeps warm her note.

Ask me no more where those stars light,
That downwards fall in dead of night;
For in your eyes they sit, and there
Fixéd become, as in their sphere.

Ask me no more if east or west
The phoenix builds her spicy nest;
For unto you at last she flies,
And in your fragrant bosom dies.

THOMAS CAREW (?1598-1639)

42 *That Night For Ever Dear*

NEALCE, be that night for ever dear,
  The night that laid you first upon my heart.
Dear be the couch, the quiet burning lamp,
  And you, so tender, come into my power.
Still let us love, although the years be hasting,
And use the hours that brief delay is wasting.
Old love should last: O Love, do thou forfend
That what was swift begun, were swift to end.

PETRONIUS ARBITER (c27BC-AD66)
TRANSLATED BY HELEN WADDELL

43 *Wild Nights*

WILD Nights—Wild Nights!
Were I with thee,
Wild Nights should be
Our luxury!

Futile—the Winds—
To a Heart in port—
Done with the Compass—
Done with the Chart!

Rowing in Eden—
Ah, the Sea!
Might I but moor—Tonight —
In thee!

EMILY DICKINSON (1830-1886)

44 *from Lines Composed A Few Miles Above Tintern Abbey*

… THEREFORE let the moon
Shine on thee in thy solitary walk;
And let the misty mountain-winds be free
To blow against thee: and, in after years,
When these wild ecstasies shall be matured
Into a sober pleasure; when thy mind
Shall be a mansion for all lovely forms,
Thy memory be as a dwelling place
For all sweet sounds and harmonies; oh! then,
If solitude, or fear, or pain, or grief
Should be thy portion, with what healing thoughts
Of tender joy wilt thou remember me,
And these my exhortations! Nor, perchance—
If I should be where I no more can hear
Thy voice, nor catch from thy wild eyes these gleams
Of past existence—wilt thou then forget
That on the banks of this delightful stream
We stood together; and that I, so long
A worshipper of Nature, hither came
Unwearied in that service: rather say
With warmer love—oh! with far deeper zeal
Of holier love …

WILLIAM WORDSWORTH (1770-1850)

45 *After You Speak*

AFTER you speak
And what you meant
Is plain,
My eyes
Meet yours that mean—
With your cheeks and hair—
Something more wise,
More dark,
And far different.
Even so the lark
Loves dust
And nestles in it
The minute
Before he must
Soar in lone flight
So far,
Like a black star
He seems—
A mote
Of singing dust
Afloat
Above,
That dreams
And sheds no light.
I know your lust
Is love.

EDWARD THOMAS (1878-1917)

46 *A Birthday*

MY HEART is like a singing bird
  Whose nest is in a watered shoot;
My heart is like an apple tree
  Whose boughs are bent with thickset fruit;
My heart is like a rainbow shell
  That paddles in a halcyon sea;
My heart is gladder than all these
  Because my love is come to me.

Raise me a dais of silk and down;
  Hang it with vair and purple dyes;
Carve it in doves, and pomegranates,
  And peacocks with a hundred eyes;
Work it in gold and silver grapes,
  In leaves and silver fleurs-de-lys;
Because the birthday of my life
  Is come, my love is come to me.

CHRISTINA ROSSETTI (1830-1894)

47 *My Wife, from Songs of Travel*

TRUSTY, dusky, vivid, true,
With eyes of gold and bramble-dew,
  Steel-true and blade-straight,
    The great artificer
  Made my mate.

Honour, anger, valour, fire;
A love that life could never tire,
  Death quench or evil stir,
    The mighty master
  Gave to her.

Teacher, tender, comrade, wife,
A fellow-farer true through life,
  Heart-whole and soul-free
    The august father
  Gave to me.

ROBERT LOUIS STEVENSON (1850-1894)

48 *My True-Love Hath My Heart*

MY TRUE-LOVE hath my heart and I have his,
By just exchange one for the other given:
I hold his dear, and mine he cannot miss;
There never was a better bargain driven.
His heart in me keeps me and him in one;
My heart in him his thoughts and senses guides:
He loves my heart, for once it was his own,
I cherish his because in me it bides.
His heart his wound received from my sight,
My heart was wounded with his wounded heart;
For as from me on him his hurt did light,
So still, methought, in me his hurt did smart.
Both equal hurt, in this change sought our bliss:
My true love hath my heart and I have his.

SIR PHILIP SIDNEY (1554-1586)

49 *To Jane*

THE keen stars were twinkling,
And the fair moon was rising among them,
Dear Jane.
The guitar was tinkling,
But the notes were not sweet till you sung them
Again.

As the moon's soft splendour
O'er the faint cold starlight of Heaven
Is thrown,
So your voice most tender
To the strings without soul had then given
Its own.

The stars will awaken,
Though the moon sleep a full hour later
To-night;
No leaf will be shaken
Whilst the dews of your melody scatter
Delight.

Though the sound overpowers,
Sing again, with your dear voice revealing
A tone
Of some world far from ours,
Where music and moonlight and feeling
Are one.

PERCY BYSSHE SHELLEY (1792-1822)

50 *from Twelfth Night*

IF MUSIC be the food of love, play on,
Give me excess of it, that, surfeiting,
The appetite may sicken and so die.
That strain again! It had a dying fall;
O! it came o'er my ear like the sweet sound
That breathes upon a bank of violets,
Stealing and giving odour! Enough, no more;
'Tis not so sweet now as it was before.
O spirit of love! how quick and fresh art thou,
That, notwithstanding thy capacity
Receiveth as the sea, nought enters there,
Of what validity and pitch soe'er,
But falls into abatement and low price
Even in a minute. So full of shapes is fancy,
That it alone is high fantastical.

WILLIAM SHAKESPEARE (1564-1616)

51 *Time of Roses*

IT WAS not in the Winter
  Our loving lot was cast;
It was the time of roses—
  We pluck'd them as we pass'd!
That churlish season never frown'd
  On early lovers yet:
O no—the world was newly crown'd
  With flowers when first we met!
'Twas twilight, and I bade you go,
  But still you held me fast;
It was the time of roses—
  We pluck'd them as we pass'd!

THOMAS HOOD (1799-1845)

52 *Meeting at Night*

THE gray sea and the long black land;
And the yellow half-moon large and low;
And the startled little waves that leap
In fiery ringlets from their sleep,
As I gain the cove with pushing prow,
And quench its speed i' the slushy sand.

Then a mile of warm sea-scented beach;
Three fields to cross till a farm appears;
A tap at the pane, the quick sharp scratch
And blue spurt of a lighted match,
And a voice less loud, through its joys and fears,
Than the two hearts beating each to each!

ROBERT BROWNING (1812-1889)

53 *A Slice Of Wedding Cake*

WHY have such scores of lovely, gifted girls
    Married impossible men?
Simple self-sacrifice may be ruled out,
    And missionary endeavour, nine times out of ten.

Repeat 'impossible men': not merely rustic,
    Foul-tempered or depraved
(Dramatic foils chosen to show the world
    How well women behave, and always have behaved).

Impossible men: idle, illiterate,
    Self-pitying, dirty, sly,
For whose appearance even in City parks
    Excuses must be made to casual passers-by.

Has God's supply of tolerable husbands
    Fallen, in fact, so low?
Or do I always over-value woman
    At the expense of man?
                                        Do I?
                                                It might be so.

ROBERT GRAVES (1895-1984)

54 *from Much Ado about Nothing*

SIGH no more, ladies, sigh no more,
  Men were deceivers ever;
One foot in sea, and one on shore,
  To one thing constant never.
    Then sigh not so,
    But let them go,
  And be you blithe and bonny,
Converting all your sounds of woe
  Into Hey nonny, nonny.

Sing no more ditties, sing no mo,
  Or dumps so dull and heavy;
The fraud of men was ever so,
  Since summer first was leavy.
    Then sigh not so,
    But let them go,
  And be you blithe and bonny,
Converting all your sounds of woe
  Into Hey, nonny, nonny.

WILLIAM SHAKESPEARE (1564-1616)

55 *Bloody Men*

BLOODY men are like bloody buses—
You wait for about a year
And as soon as one approaches your stop
Two or three others appear.

You look at them flashing their indicators,
Offering you a ride.
You're trying to read the destinations,
You haven't much time to decide.

If you make a mistake, there is no turning back.
Jump off, and you'll stand there and gaze
While the cars and the taxis and lorries go by
And the minutes, the hours, the days.

WENDY COPE (1945-)

56 *Love, What Is Love?*

LOVE—what is love? A great and aching heart;
Wrung hands; and silence; and a long despair.
Life—what is life? Upon a moorland bare
To see love coming and see love depart.

ROBERT LOUIS STEVENSON (1850-1894)

57 *from A Shropshire Lad*

WHEN I was one-and-twenty
   I heard a wise man say,
'Give crowns and pounds and guineas
   But not your heart away;
Give pearls away and rubies
   But keep your fancy free.'
But I was one-and-twenty,
   No use to talk to me.

When I was one-and-twenty
   I heard him say again,
'The heart out of the bosom
   Was never given in vain;
'Tis paid with sighs a plenty
   And sold for endless rue.'
And I am two-and-twenty
   And oh, 'tis true, 'tis true.

A E HOUSMAN (1859-1936)

58 *Love's Secret*

NEVER seek to tell thy love
Love that never told can be;
For the gentle wind doth move
Silently, invisibly.

I told my love, I told my love,
I told her all my heart,
Trembling, cold, in ghastly fears—
Ah, she did depart.

Soon as she was gone from me
A traveller came by,
Silently, invisibly—
He took her with a sigh.

WILLIAM BLAKE (1757-1827)

59 *I'm Really Very Fond*

I'M REALLY very fond of you,
he said.

I don't like fond.
It sounds like something
you would tell a dog.

Give me love,
or nothing.

Throw your fond in a pond,
I said.

But what I felt for him
was also warm, frisky,
moist-mouthed,
eager,
and could swim away

if forced to do so.

ALICE WALKER (1944-)

60 *from Amores: The Triumph of Love*

WHO is it that can tell me why my bed seems so hard
And why the bedclothes will not stay upon it?
Wherefore has this night—and oh, how long it was!—
dragged on, bringing no sleep to my eyes?
Why are my weary limbs visited with restlessness and pain?
If it were Love that had come to make me suffer,
Surely I should know it.
Or stay, what if he slips in like a thief,
What if he comes, without a word of warning,
To wound me with his cruel arts?
Yes, 'tis he! His slender arrows have pierced my heart,
And fell Love holds it like a conquered land.
Shall I yield me to him? Or shall I strive against him,
And so add fuel to this sudden flame?
Well, I will yield; burdens willingly borne do lighter weigh.

OVID (43BC-AD18)
TRANSLATED BY J LEWIS MAY

61 *Love is a Sickness*

LOVE is a sickness full of woes,
  All remedies refusing;
A plant that with most cutting grows,
  Most barren with best using.
    Why so?
More we enjoy it, more it dies;
If not enjoyed, its sighing cries
    Heigh ho!
Love is a torment of the mind,
  A tempest everlasting;
And Jove hath made it of a kind
  Not well, nor full, nor fasting.
    Why so?
More we enjoy it, more it dies;
If not enjoyed, its sighing cries
    Heigh ho!

SAMUEL DANIEL (1562-1619)

62 *Saturday Morning*

EVERYONE who made love the night before
was walking around with flashing red lights
on top of their heads—a white-haired old gentleman,
a red-faced schoolboy, a pregnant woman
who smiled at me from across the street
and gave a little secret shrug,
as if the flashing red light on her head
was a small price to pay for what she knew.

HUGO WILLIAMS (1942-)

63 *Lesbia's Sparrow*

TELL me, sparrow, you darling of my darling,
whom she plays with and fondles in her bosom,
you who peck when she offers you a finger
(beak out-thrust in a counterfeit of biting),
when that radiant star of my aspiring
turns towards you, as a pleasant little playmate,
one small bird, to console her when she suffers,
by your love to relieve her burning passion—
could I possibly play with you as she does,
could I lighten the pain that still torments me?

CATULLUS (c84BC-c54BC)
TRANSLATED BY GILBERT HIGHET

64 *from The Flea*

MARK but this flea, and mark in this,
How little that which thou deny'st me is;
Me it sucked first, and now sucks thee,
And in this flea, our two bloods mingled be;
Confess it, this cannot be said
A sin, or shame, or loss of maidenhead,
  Yet this enjoys before it woo,
  And pampered, swells with one blood made of two,
  And this, alas, is more than we would do …

JOHN DONNE (1572-1631)

65 *Isolation: To Marguerite*

WE WERE apart: yet, day by day,
I bade my heart more constant be;
I bade it keep the world away,
And grow a home for only thee:
Nor fear'd but thy love likewise grew,
Like mine, each day more tried, more true.

The fault was grave; I might have known,
What far too soon, alas, I learn'd—
The heart can bind itself alone,
And faith is often unreturn'd—
Self-sway'd our feelings ebb and swell:
Thou lov'st no more: Farewell! Farewell!

Farewell! and thou, thou lonely heart,
Which never yet without remorse
Even for a moment didst depart
From thy remote and sphered course
To haunt the place where passions reign,
Back to thy solitude again! …

MATTHEW ARNOLD (1822-1888)

66 *Sonnet 57*

BEING your slave, what should I do but tend
Upon the hours and times of your desire?
I have no precious time at all to spend
Nor services to do, till you require:

Nor dare I chide the world-without-end hour
Whilst I, my sovereign, watch the clock for you,
Nor think the bitterness of absence sour
When you have bid your servant once adieu:

Nor dare I question with my jealous thought
Where you may be, or your affairs suppose,
But like a sad slave, stay and think of nought
Save, where you are how happy you make those;—

So true a fool is love, that in your will,
Though you do any thing, he thinks no ill.

WILLIAM SHAKESPEARE (1564-1616)

67 *The Clod and the Pebble*

'LOVE seeketh not Itself to please,
Nor for itself hath any care,
But for another gives its ease,
And builds a Heaven in Hell's despair.'

So sung a little Clod of Clay
Trodden with the cattle's feet,
But a Pebble of the brook
Warbled out these metres meet:

'Love seeketh only Self to please,
To bind another to Its delight,
Joys in another's loss of ease,
And builds a Hell in Heaven's despite.'

WILLIAM BLAKE (1757-1827)

68 *from Measure for Measure*

TAKE, O take those lips away,
  That so sweetly were forsworn,
And those eyes, the break of day,
  Lights that do mislead the morn;
But my kisses bring again,
      Bring again—
Seals of love, but seal'd in vain,
      Seal'd in vain!

WILLIAM SHAKESPEARE (1564-1616)

69 *Sonnet 138*

WHEN my love swears that she is made of truth,
I do believe her, though I know she lies,
That she might think me some untutor'd youth
Unlearned in the world's false subtleties.

Thus vainly thinking that she thinks me young,
Although she knows my days are past the best,
Simply I credit her false-speaking tongue;
On both sides thus is simple truth suppressed.

But wherefore says she not she is unjust?
And wherefore say not I that I am old?
O, love's best habit is in seeming trust,
And age in love loves not to have years told.

Therefore I lie with her, and she with me,
And in our faults by lies we flattered be.

WILLIAM SHAKESPEARE (1564-1616)

70 *I Do Not Love Thee*

I DO not love thee!—no! I do not love thee!
And yet when thou art absent I am sad;
And envy even the bright blue sky above thee,
Whose quiet stars may see thee and be glad.

I do not love thee!—yet, I know not why,
Whate'er thou dost seems still well done, to me:
And often in my solitude I sigh
That those I do love are not more like thee!

I do not love thee!—yet, when thou art gone,
I hate the sound (though those who speak be dear)
Which breaks the lingering echo of the tone
Thy voice of music leaves upon my ear.

I do not love thee!—yet thy speaking eyes,
With their deep, bright, and most expressive blue,
Between me and the midnight heaven arise,
Oftener than any eyes I ever knew.

I know I do not love thee! yet, alas!
Others will scarcely trust my candid heart;
And oft I catch them smiling as they pass,
Because they see me gazing where thou art.

CAROLINE NORTON (1808-1877)

71 *The Hill*

BREATHLESS, we flung us on the windy hill,
Laughed in the sun, and kissed the lovely grass.
You said, 'Through glory and ecstasy we pass;
Wind, sun, and earth remain, the birds sing still,
When we are old, are old ...' 'And when we die
All's over that is ours; and life burns on
Through other lovers, other lips,' said I,
'Heart of my heart, our heaven is now, is won!'

'We are Earth's best, that learnt her lesson here.
Life is our cry. We have kept the faith!' we said;
'We shall go down with unreluctant tread
Rose-crowned into the darkness!' ... Proud we were,
And laughed, that had such brave true things to say.
—And then you suddenly cried, and turned away.

RUPERT BROOKE (1887-1915)

72 *from Achillis Amatores: Melting Ice*

LOVE is a pain with purest joy combined:
No bad comparison to Love I'll find—
Boys when the heavens are frosty, in a trice
Will take a handful of hard frozen ice;
And first it's all delight and wonder, then
The lump no more will be let go again,
Nor yet be pretty treasure to retain.
Even so with lovers, when their hearts require
To love and not-love by the same desire.

SOPHOCLES (495BC-406BC) TRANSLATED BY J S PHILLIMORE

73 *First Love*

I NE'ER was struck before that hour
With love so sudden and so sweet.
Her face it bloomed like a sweet flower
And stole my heart away complete.
My face turned pale as deadly pale.
My legs refused to walk away,
And when she looked 'what could I ail?'
My life and all seemed turned to clay.

And then my blood rushed to my face
And took my sight away.
The trees and bushes round the place
Seemed midnight at noonday.
I could not see a single thing,
Words from my eyes did start.
They spoke as chords do from the string,
And blood burnt round my heart.

Are flowers the winter's choice?
Is love's bed always snow?
She seemed to hear my silent voice
And love's appeal to know.
I never saw so sweet a face
As that I stood before:
My heart has left its dwelling-place
And can return no more.

JOHN CLARE (1793-1864)

74 *from Romeo and Juliet*

O ROMEO, Romeo! wherefore art thou Romeo?
Deny thy father and refuse thy name;
Or, if thou wilt not, be but sworn my love,
And I'll no longer be a Capulet . . .

'Tis but thy name that is my enemy;
Thou art thyself, though not a Montague.
What's Montague? it is nor hand nor foot,
Nor arm, nor face, nor any other part
Belonging to a man. O, be some other name!
What's in a name? that which we call a rose
By any other name would smell as sweet;
So Romeo would, were he not Romeo call'd,
Retain that dear perfection which he owes
Without that title. Romeo, doff thy name;
And for thy name, which is no part of thee,
Take all myself.

WILLIAM SHAKESPEARE (1564-1616)

75 *I Hid my Love*

I HID my love when young till I
Couldn't bear the buzzing of a fly;
I hid my love to my despite
Till I could not bear to look at light:
I dare not gaze upon her face
But left her memory in each place;
Where'er I saw a wild flower lie
I kissed and bade my love good-bye.

I met her in the greenest dells,
Where dewdrops pearl the wood bluebells;
The lost breeze kissed her bright blue eye,
The bee kissed and went singing by,
A sunbeam found a passage there,
A gold chain round her neck so fair;
As secret as the wild bee's song
She lay there all the summer long.

I hid my love in field and town
Till e'en the breeze would knock me down;
The bees seemed singing ballads o'er,
The fly's bass turned a lion's roar;
And even silence found a tongue,
To haunt me all the summer long;
The riddle nature could not prove
Was nothing else but secret love.

JOHN CLARE (1793-1864)

76 *The Bridesmaid*

WHY am I dressed in these beautiful clothes?
What is the matter with me?
I've been the bridesmaid for twenty-two brides:
This time'll make twenty-three.
Twenty-two ladies I've helped off the shelf,
No doubt it seems a bit strange:
Being the bridesmaid is no good to me;
And I think I could do with a change.

Why am I always the bridesmaid?
Never the blushing bride?
Ding-dong! Wedding bells
Only ring for other gels;
But some fine day—
Oh, let it be soon!—
I shall wake up in the morning
On my own honeymoon.

CHARLES COLLINS AND FRED W LEIGH (c1917)

77 *from To Lizbie Browne*

DEAR Lizbie Browne,
Where are you now?
In sun, in rain?—
Or is your brow
Past joy, past pain,
Dear Lizbie Browne? ...

And, Lizbie Browne,
Who else had hair
Bay-red as yours,
Or flesh so fair
Bred out of doors,
Sweet Lizbie Browne? ...

Ay, Lizbie Browne,
So swift your life,
And mine so slow,
You were a wife
Ere I could show
Love, Lizbie Browne.

But, Lizbie Browne,
I let you slip;
Shaped not a sign;
Touched never your lip
With lip of mine,
Lost Lizbie Browne!

THOMAS HARDY (1840-1928)

78 *Odes Book 1, No 5*

WHAT slim youngster, his hair dripping with fragrant oil,
Makes hot love to you now, Pyrrha, ensconced in a
  Snug cave curtained with roses?
    Who lays claim to that casually

Chic blonde hair in a braid? Soon he'll be scolding the
Gods, whose promise, like yours, failed him, and gaping at
  Black winds making his ocean's
    Fair face unrecognisable.

He's still credulous, though, hugging the prize he thinks
Pure gold, shining and fond, his for eternity.
  Ah, poor fool, but the breeze plays
    Tricks. Doomed, all who would venture to

Sail that glittering sea. Fixed to the temple wall,
My plaque tells of an old sailor who foundered and,
  Half-drowned, hung up his clothes to
    Neptune, lord of the element.

HORACE (65BC-8BC)
TRANSLATED BY JAMES MICHIE

79 *Heart! We Will Forget Him*

HEART! We will forget him!
You and I—tonight!
You may forget the warmth he gave—
I will forget the light!

When you have done, pray tell me
That I may straight begin!
Haste! lest while you're lagging
I remember him!

EMILY DICKINSON (1830-1886)

80 *Farewell to Love*

SINCE there's no help, come let us kiss and part,—
Nay I have done, you get no more of me;
And I am glad, yea, glad with all my heart,
That thus so cleanly I myself can free;

Shake hands for ever, cancel all our vows,
And when we meet at any time again,
Be it not seen in either of our brows
That we one jot of former love retain.

Now at the last gasp of love's latest breath,
When his pulse failing, passion speechless lies,
When faith is kneeling by his bed of death,
And innocence is closing up his eyes,—

Now if thou woulds't, when all have given him over,
From death to life thou might'st him yet recover.

MICHAEL DRAYTON (1563-1631)

81 *Who Ever Felt As I?*

MOTHER, I cannot mind my wheel;
   My fingers ache, my lips are dry:
O, if you felt the pain I feel!
   But O, who ever felt as I?
No longer could I doubt him true—
   All other men may use deceit;
He always said my eyes were blue,
   And often swore my lips were sweet.

W S LANDOR (1775-1864)

82 *The Darling Letters*

SOME keep them in shoeboxes away from the light,
sore memories blinking out as the lid lifts,
their own recklessness written all over them. *My own …*
Private jokes, no longer comprehended, pull their punchlines,
fall flat in the gaps between endearments. *What*
Are you wearing?

Don't ever change.
They start with *Darling*; end in recriminations,
absence, sense of loss. Even now, the fist's bud flowers
into trembling, the fingers trace each line and see
the future then. *Always …* Nobody burns them,
The *Darling* letters, stiff in their cardboard coffins.

Babykins … We all had strange names
which make us blush, as though we'd murdered
someone under an alias, long ago. *I'll die*
without you. Die. Once in a while, alone,
we take them out to read again, the heart thudding
like a spade on buried bones.

CAROL ANN DUFFY (1955-)

83 *Loss*

THE day he moved out was terrible—
That evening she went through hell.
His absence wasn't a problem
But the corkscrew had gone as well.

WENDY COPE (1945-)

84 *The End of Love*

THE end of love should be a big event.
It should involve the hiring of a hall.
Why the hell not? It happens to us all.
Why should it pass without acknowledgement?

Suits should be dry-cleaned, invitations sent.
Whatever form it takes—a tiff, a brawl—
The end of love should be a big event.
It should involve the hiring of a hall.

Better than the unquestioning descent
Into the trap of silence, than the crawl
From visible to hidden, door to wall.

Get the announcement made, the money spent.
The end of love should be a big event.
It should involve the hiring of a hall.

SOPHIE HANNAH (1971-)

85 *A Woman's Work*

WILL you forgive me that I did not run
to welcome you as you came in the door?
Forgive I did not sew your buttons on
and left a mess strewn on the kitchen floor?
A woman's work is never done
and there is more.

The things I did I should have left undone
the things I lost that I could not restore;
Will you forgive I wasn't any fun?
Will you forgive I couldn't give you more?
A woman's work is never done
and there is more.

I never finished what I had begun,
I could not keep the promises I swore,
so we fought battles neither of us won
and I said 'Sorry!' and you banged the door.
A woman's work is never done
and there is more.

But in the empty space now you are gone
I find the time I didn't have before.
I lock the house and walk out to the sun
where the sea beats upon a wider shore
and woman's work is never done,
not any more.

DOROTHY NIMMO (d2001)

86 *My cat and i*

GIRLS are simply the prettiest things
My cat and i believe
And we're always saddened
When it's time for them to leave

We watch them titivating
(that often takes a while)
And though they keep us waiting
My cat and i just smile

We like to see them to the door
Say how sad it couldn't last
Then my cat and i go back inside
And talk about the past

ROGER MCGOUGH (1937-)

87 *A Lady*

YOU are beautiful and faded
Like an old opera tune
Played upon a harpsichord;
Or like the sun-flooded silks
Of an eighteenth-century boudoir.
In your eyes
Smoulder the fallen roses of out-lived minutes,
And the perfume of your soul
Is vague and suffusing,
With the pungence of sealed spice-jars.
Your half-tones delight me,
And I grow mad with gazing
At your blent colours.
My vigour is a new-minted penny,
Which I cast at your feet.
Gather it up from the dust,
That its sparkle may amuse you.

AMY LOWELL (1874-1925)

88 *Helen, from Household Poems*

AND you, Helen, what should I give you?
So many things I would give you
Had I an infinite great store
Offered me and I stood before
To choose. I would give you youth,
All kinds of loveliness and truth,
A clear eye as good as mine,
Lands, waters, flowers, wine,
As many children as your heart
Might wish for, a far better art
Than mine can be, all you have lost
Upon the travelling waters tossed,
Or given to me. If I could choose
Freely in that great treasure-house
Anything from any shelf,
I would give you back yourself,
And power to discriminate
What you want and want it not too late,
Many fair days free from care
And heart to enjoy both foul and fair,
And myself, too, if I could find
Where it lay hidden and it proved kind.

EDWARD THOMAS (1878-1917)

89 *Kissing*

THE young are walking on the riverbank,
arms around each other's waist and shoulders,
pretending to be looking at the waterlilies
and what might be a nest of some kind, over
there, which two who are clamped together
mouth to mouth have forgotten about.
The others, making courteous detours
around them, talk, stop talking, kiss.
They can see no one older than themselves.
It's their river. They've got all day.

Seeing's not everything. At this very
moment the middle-aged are kissing
in the backs of taxis, on the way
to airports and stations. Their mouths and tongues
are soft and powerful and as moist as ever.
Their hands are not inside each other's clothes
(because of the driver) but locked so tightly
together that it hurts: it may leave marks
on their not of course youthful skin, which they won't
notice. They too may have futures.

FLEUR ADCOCK (1934-)

90 *from The Two Gentlemen of Verona*

WHO is Silvia? what is she,
   That all our swains commend her?
Holy, fair, and wise is she;
   The heaven such grace did lend her,
That she might admirèd be.

Is she kind as she is fair?
   For beauty lives with kindness.
Love doth to her eyes repair,
   To help him of his blindness,
And, being helped, inhabits there.

Then to Silvia let us sing,
   That Silvia is excelling;
She excels each mortal thing
   Upon the dull earth dwelling:
To her let us garlands bring.

WILLIAM SHAKESPEARE (1564-1616)

91 *Jeanie with the Light Brown Hair*

I DREAM of Jeanie with the light brown hair,
Borne, like a vapour, on the summer air;
I see her tripping where the bright streams play,
Happy as the daisies that dance on her way.
Many were the wild notes her merry voice would pour,
Many were the blithe birds that warbled them o'er:
Oh! I dream of Jeanie with the light brown hair,
Floating, like a vapor, on the soft summer air.

I sigh for Jeanie, but her light form strayed
Far from the fond hearts 'round her native glade;
Her smiles have vanished and her sweet songs flown,
Flitting like the dreams that have cheered us and gone.
Now the nodding wild flowers may wither on the shore
While her gentle fingers will cull them no more:
Oh! I sigh for Jeanie with the light brown hair,
Floating, like a vapour, on the soft summer air.

STEPHEN FOSTER (1826-1864)

92 *The Smile*

THERE is a smile of love,
and there is a smile of deceit;
and there is a smile of smiles,
in which these two smiles meet.
(And there is a frown of hate,
and there is a frown of disdain;
and there is a frown of frowns
which you strive to forget in vain,
For it sticks in the heart's deep core,
and it sticks in the deep backbone.)
And no smile that ever was smiled,
but only one smile alone—
That betwixt the cradle and grave
it only once smiled can be,
but when it once is smiled
there's an end to all misery.

WILLIAM BLAKE (1757-1827)

93 *from Hero and Leander*

… IT LIES not in our power to love, or hate,
For will in us is over-rul'd by fate.
When two are stripped, long ere the course begin,
We wish that one should love, the other win;
And one especially do we affect
Of two gold ingots, like in each respect.
The reason no man knows; let it suffice,
What we behold is censured by our eyes.
Where both deliberate the love is slight:
Who ever loved that loved not at first sight? …

CHRISTOPHER MARLOWE (1564-1593)

94 *To ..*

ONE word is too often profaned
 For me to profane it,
One feeling too falsely disdain'd
 For thee to disdain it;
One hope is too like despair
 For prudence to smother,
And Pity from thee more dear
 Than that from another.

I can give not what men call love;
 But wilt thou accept not
The worship the heart lifts above
 And the heavens reject not,—
The desire of the moth for the star,
 Of the night for the morrow,
The devotion to something afar
 From the sphere of our sorrow?

PERCY BYSSHE SHELLEY (1792-1822)

95 *Somewhere or Other*

SOMEWHERE or other there must surely be
The face not seen, the voice not heard,
The heart that not yet—never yet—ah me!
Made answer to my word.

Somewhere or other, may be near or far;
Past land and sea, clean out of sight;
Beyond the wandering moon, beyond the star
That tracks her night by night.

Somewhere or other, may be far or near;
With just a wall, a hedge, between;
With just the last leaves of the dying year
Fallen on a turf grown green.

CHRISTINA ROSSETTI (1830-1894)

98 *A Statue of Love*

WHO sculptured Love beside this fountain?—Fool!
To think with water such a flame to cool!

ZENODOTUS (325BC-?260BC) TRANSLATED BY H WELLESLEY

99 *The Lowest Trees Have Tops*

THE lowest trees have tops, the ant her gall,
The fly her spleen, the little spark his heat;
The slender hairs cast shadows, though but small,
And bees have stings, although they be not great;
    Seas have their source, and so have shallow springs,
    And love is love, in beggars and in kings.

Where waters smoothest run, deep are the fords;
The dial stirs, yet none perceives it move;
The firmest faith is in the fewest words;
The turtles cannot sing, and yet they love.
    True hearts have eyes and ears, no tongues to speak;
    They hear and see, and sigh, and then they break.

SIR EDWARD DYER (?-1607)

100 *Sonnet 116*

LET ME not to the marriage of true minds
Admit impediments. Love is not love
Which alters when it alteration finds,
Or bends with the remover to remove.

O, no! it is an ever-fixèd mark,
That looks on tempests and is never shaken;
It is the star to every wand'ring bark,
Whose worth's unknown, although his height be taken.

Love's not Time's fool, though rosy lips and cheeks
Within his bending sickle's compass come;
Love alters not with his brief hours and weeks,
But bears it out even to the edge of doom.

If this be error, and upon me proved,
I never writ, nor no man ever loved.

WILLIAM SHAKESPEARE (1564-1616)

FIRST LINE INDEX

Acknowledgments

relationships guru. I have not 'made it
sex and relationships. I've made mistal
ed up just as much as the next person.
u don't think that *Pure* is the wise words
Marshall but the outworking of the grip o
ace in each of our lives.
'life cycle of *Pure*', I've been so grateful for
Rhodes for caring enough about the Christia
t Nottingham to suggest we put on a course
o people with what God says about
ships: the birth of *Pure*.
than Clark and Pod Bhogal, colleagues
rdinaires, who saw the course developed and
. I am indebted to you both.
(now) husband Phil for emailing me for a copy of
ure course . . . even though you had no intention of
lly reading it. Your chat-up line obviously worked.
ike Partridge, Pod Bhogal (again!), Jude Hahn,
ham Daniels, Ali Price and Helen Jenner: Thank
so much for your invaluable thoughts and critique
ough *Pure*'s growing pains!
Eleanor Trotter and Sandra Byatt at IVP have been
nderful editors and have gently and expertly guided
e through the business of being a first-time mum (of
book, that is!).

ACKNOWLEDGEMENTS

The publishers would like to acknowledge the following for permission to reproduce copyright poems in this collection.

Fleur Adcock, 'Kissing'. Reprinted with the permission of Bloodaxe Books Ltd.

John Betjeman, 'A Subaltern's Love-story', from Collected Poems, 2001. Reprinted with the permission of John Murray (Publishers) Ltd.

Catullus, 'Lesbia's Sparrow', 'To Lesbia' & 'Life & Love' from Poets in a Landscape, Gilbert Highet (trans.). Reprinted with the permission of Prion Books Ltd.

Wendy Cope, 'Loss' and 'Bloody Men', from Serious Concerns. Reprinted with the permission of Faber & Faber.

Dante 'La Vita Nuova XXI: How Beatrice Awakens Love' (trans. A S Kline). Copyright A.S. Kline 2000. Further translations may be found at the Ovid and Others Internet Web site at http://www.tkline.freeserve.co.uk and the Dante and Others Web site at http://www.tonykline.free-online.co.uk

Carol Ann Duffy, 'The Darling Letters' is taken from The Other Country by Carol Ann Duffy published by Anvil Press Poetry in 1990. Reprinted with the permission of the publishers.

Robert Graves, 'Symptoms of Love' and 'A Slice of Wedding Cake' from The Complete Poems in One Volume, Beryl Graves & Dunstan Ward (ed.), Carcanet Press Limited 2000. Reprinted with permission from Carcanet Press Ltd.

Sophie Hannah, 'The End Of Love'. Reprinted with permission from Carcanet Press Ltd.

A E Housman, from 'A Shropshire Lad' from The Collected Poems of A E Housman (Holt, Rinehart and Winston, Inc.). Reprinted with permission of The Society of Authors as literary representative of the Estate of A E Housman.

Roger McGough, 'My Cat and I'. Reprinted by permission of PFD on behalf of: Roger McGough ©Roger McGough: as printed in the original volume.

Ms Of Beauvais, 'By Day Mine Eyes', Helen Waddell (trans.) from Medieval Latin Lyrics, Helen Waddell (ed.), Constable & Robinson Publishing Ltd. Reprinted with the permission of the publishers.

Mss of Salzburg, Canterbury & Limoges, 'Come Sweetheart Come', Helen Waddell (trans.) from Medieval Latin Lyrics, Helen Waddell (ed.), Constable & Robinson Publishing Ltd. Reprinted with the permission of the publishers.

Ms Of St Remy at Rheims, 'Young and Gold-Haired', Helen Waddell (trans.) from Medieval Latin Lyrics, Helen Waddell (ed.), Constable & Robinson Publishing Ltd. Reprinted with the permission of the publishers.

Dorothy Nimmo, 'A Woman's Work'. Reprinted with the permission of Ms Margaret Nimmo.

Ovid, 'Amores 1.5 Corinna in an Afternoon' (trans. A.S. Kline). Copyright A.S. Kline 2000. Further translations may be found at the Ovid and Others Internet Web site at http://www.tkline.freeserve.co.uk and the Dante and Others Web site at http://www.tonykline.free-online.co.uk

Alice Walker, 'I'm Really Very Fond', from Horses Make A Landscape Look More Beautiful, The Women's Press. Reprinted with the permission of David Higham Associates.

Hugo Williams, 'Saturday Morning' from Dock Leaves. Reprinted with the permission of Faber & Faber.

W B Yeats, 'Love Song' from The Poems of W B Yeats: A New Edition, edited by R J Finneran. Copyright ©1940 by Georgie Yeats, renewed 1968 by Bertha Georgie Yeats. Reprinted with the permission of A P Watt Ltd., on behalf of Michael Yeats.

Although the publishers have tried to contact all copyright holders before publication, this has not proved possible in every case. If notified, the publisher will be pleased to make any necessary arrangements.

'We are reaping the conse
choices in terms of sexuall
pregnancy, abortion and br
Christian young people need
encouragement than ever to
great temptation to comprom
this challenge. It is refreshingly
and has been thoroughly tested

Peter Saunders, General Secretar
Christian Medical Fellowship

I am not a
the area o
and muck
I hope yo
of Linda
gospel gr
In the
Jonty
Union a
to equip
relation
Jona
extrao
honed
My
the P
actua
M
Gra
you
thr

wo
m
a

pure

Sex and relationships God's way

Linda Marshall

INTER-VARSITY PRESS
Norton Street, Nottingham NG7 3HR, England
Email: ivp@ivpbooks.com
Website: www.ivpbooks.com

© Linda Marshall, 2005

Linda Marshall has asserted her right under the Copyright, Design and Patents Act, 1988, to be identified as Author of this work.

All rights reserved. No part of this publication may be reproduced, stored in a retrieval system, or transmitted, in any form or by any means, electronic, mechanical, photocopying, recording or otherwise, without the prior permission of the publisher or the Copyright Licensing Agency.

Unless otherwise stated, Scripture quotations in the text are taken from the Holy Bible, New International Version. Copyright © 1973, 1978, 1984 by International Bible Society. Used by permission of Hodder & Stoughton, a division of Hodder Headline Ltd. All rights reserved. 'NIV' is a trademark of International Bible Society. UK trademark number 1448790.

Scripture quotations on the back cover are taken from the Contemporary English Version Bible, published by HarperCollins Publishers, © 1997 British and Foreign Bible. Used by permission.

First published 2005
Reprinted 2006, 2007, 2009, 2010
Reprinted in this format 2010

British Library Cataloguing in Publication Data
A catalogue record for this book is available from the British Library.

ISBN: 978–1–84474–505–0

Set in Monotype Dante
Typeset in Great Britain by CRB Associates, Potterhanworth, Lincolnshire
Printed in Great Britain by Ashford Colour Press, Gosport, Hampshire

Inter-Varsity Press publishes Christian books that are true to the Bible and that communicate the gospel, develop discipleship and strengthen the church for its mission in the world.

Inter-Varsity Press is closely linked with the Universities and Colleges Christian Fellowship, a student movement connecting Christian Unions in universities and colleges throughout Great Britain, and a member movement of the International Fellowship of Evangelical Students. Website: www.uccf.org.uk

Foreword

'You've tried so hard to be someone that you forgot who you are.'

Do you ever get tired of being different? Do you feel that the cost of rescuing people is too great to bear? Do you look in your wardrobe and wonder if you should pull on clothes that mark you out or clothes that blend? Do you find a conflict between your new identity and being successful and popular?

If you answered 'yes' to all these questions, you may be Peter Parker in *Spiderman 2*. (The quotation above comes from Chapter 10 of the DVD, if you're interested!) In the movie Parker grows tired of being a superhero, begins to lose his special powers, resents his calling and throws his special suit into the dustbin. Despite his best efforts, he is unable to find peace. As the movie progresses he realizes that he must embrace his true identity and be willing to make whatever personal sacrifices that entails.

If you answered 'yes' to some of the questions above, you may be a Christian. Christians have a new identity which conflicts with our natural agenda, plans and desires. It is not always easy living up to who we are. Old habits die hard; we can be painfully aware of our hypocrisy and failure and tempted to give up. Yet the truth is that we have a new identity and a new destiny. At the heart of this identity is the call to purity. If we are to be true to our calling and live with integrity, we must be pure.

'Pure' is a word our culture uses in different ways. When applied to cosmetics or food, it is an attractive adjective. In this usage 'pure' means 'natural' and is defined by the absence of preservatives, colouring, flavouring, sweeteners or artificial additives. It adds value and is often a premium brand.

When applied to people, 'pure' is often seen less positively. Many see purity as a negative attribute, making a person less fun, less interesting, less switched-on. I remember, as a student, going to a talk entitled 'Passion and Purity' and being rather disappointed that it wasn't a choice between the two but some kind of package deal!

But 'pure' is not a dirty word. We badly need a new vision of purity that recognizes the high value of personal holiness.

Purity is not something that comes naturally to us. It is not defined primarily by the absence of anything but is a positive quality, produced by God through relationship with him. As people, our characters are flawed, our motives are tarnished and our orientation is fundamentally selfish. Our new identity in Christ calls us to live distinctive lives characterized by a radical attitude to money, sex, image and work.

The reality of the gospel is demonstrated through the differences evidenced in the Christian community. The key to authentic Christian witness is not that we blend in and blur but that we stand out. I believe it is only through the clear manifestation of the difference that Christ makes that we will make a lasting impact in our communities and in the world.

Pure will challenge you to lead a distinctive life. It will help you to avoid compromise and to get excited about the opportunities and the adventure of a life lived well.

Pure will encourage you to embrace your true identity in Christ. It will be of practical help as you engage with real issues. I would encourage you to read it at the same time as a friend and to chat through the implications as honestly as you can.

You're not Spiderman. But you do have a different agenda from the people around you. You have a new calling and mission for your life. At the very heart of this is the call to be pure as God is pure.

You are actually much more special than any superhero. A different Peter put it this way:

> You are a chosen people, a royal priesthood, a holy nation, a people belonging to God, that you may declare the praises of him who called you out of darkness into his wonderful light. Once you were not a people, but now you are the people of God; once you had not received mercy, but now you have received mercy.
> (1 Peter 2:9–10)

Peter spells out the implications of this glorious new identity in the verses immediately following:

> Dear friends, I urge you, as aliens and strangers in the world, to abstain from sinful desires, which war against your soul. Live such good lives among the pagans that, though they accuse you of doing wrong,

> they may see your good deeds and glorify God on the day he visits us.
> (1 Peter 2:11–12)

May *Pure* inspire you, and may your purity inspire others to meet the One who is, and always has been, pure.

The world is full of people in need of rescue. You don't need to put on a mask to be a hero.

Don't try so hard to be someone that you forget who you are. Be pure.

Nigel D. Pollock
National Director of Tertiary Students Christian Fellowship, New Zealand

Introduction

Why pure?

She couldn't believe it as she watched the thin, blue line appear. She was pregnant. Oh my goodness, she was pregnant. Her disbelief was followed by horror. How would her parents and friends react? She was the Bible study group leader, and now everyone would know what she and her boyfriend had been doing. She thought back to how they had convinced themselves that something that felt so right couldn't be wrong. After all, they really loved each other. It seemed the right way to show it. And now it was wrong. All wrong . . .

Paul's lazy Friday night had mostly involved watching TV. By this time all his housemates had gone to bed, but he just wanted to catch the end of the film, he told himself. Now the film had ended and the adverts had come on. 'Adverts are boring,' he told himself. 'I'll just have a look to see what's on the other side.' He'd only been watching for a bit when Dave suddenly walked in. Paul made the usual dive for the remote, but he just couldn't find the channel button in time. 'Gutted!' he thought, but he wasn't sure whether that was because he knew he shouldn't have been watching that sort of film or because he'd been discovered. Dave looked at Paul in disgust, shut the door firmly and tramped upstairs. Paul sat up straight, turned off the TV and put his head in his hands. Again . . .

'Not another wedding invitation,' Sally sighed as she tossed it on to her bed. She was fed up being single. Ever since she had become a Christian two years ago, there had been no action on the man front. She had always had a boyfriend until then and loads of attention. She hadn't even had so much as an offer – well, not from any Christian man anyway. What was God playing at? Was this some sort of cruel joke? She'd been waiting for God to give her the desires of her heart, and now she was going to take matters into her own hands. 'I'm fed up waiting. I am not going to die an old spinster!' Sally thought to herself as she lifted her phone to text her ex-boyfriend . . .

How do you find being a Christian in the sex-mad society we live in? Do you find it hard to live a distinctive life? Do you find that your past is hard to shift? Do you feel exhausted at the fight within yourself? Do you feel like you're the only Christian who struggles with the things that you do? Or are you surprised when you discover that a Christian friend is also finding it hard to remain sexually pure?

Sit down for a moment. Forty per cent of Christian students have experienced genital intercourse, oral sex or mutual masturbation. Do you find that shocking? Perhaps you thought you were the only one. In fact, sex and relationships is a massive issue for many of us. It can be an issue surrounded in shame, guilt and helplessness, and we don't know where to turn.

Perhaps you've had some teaching on sex and relationships. You might have had a session at your church's youth group. You might have heard a sermon on it once. Perhaps you feel the same as John, aged nineteen, who said, 'I've had loads of teaching on the "these are the things you should and shouldn't do" stuff, but to be honest, I'm not really sure why I should or shouldn't do them.' That's a common feeling for many people.

As Christians we believe that we come to faith in Jesus through the gospel and that we should keep on living the Christian life in the same way, through the gospel: 'So then, just as you received Christ Jesus as Lord, continue to live in him, rooted and built up in him, strengthened in the faith as you were taught, and overflowing with thankfulness' (Colossians 2:6–7). The good news of Jesus' death on the cross and his resurrection should affect every area of our lives, but we're often not quite sure how that works in practice. It should affect our work life, the way we relate to our parents, our thoughts, our attitude to money and our love life.

As we go through *Pure* together, we will be confronted with what God says in his Word about how we are to live in the light of that gospel. We will start on a journey where we will discover God's plan for sex and relationships. 'How can a young man keep his way pure? By living according to [God's] word' (Psalm 119:9). God actually has a whole lot to say about remaining pure in our relationships. There are chapters and verses devoted to the subject, so they're probably worth looking at! As we hear what God has to say, we will understand better *why* his way is best, and so we will be able to shine out like stars in the midst of a very, very dark world.

When we read God's Word we experience different things. Sometimes we are illuminated and find ourselves caught up in praise. Sometimes our understanding grows and we want to express our joy. Sometimes we feel challenged and may be reluctant to take on board what God is saying. And sometimes it is

painful as God rebukes us and disciplines us.
2 Timothy 3:16–17 says that God's Word will equip us for 'every good work'.

Let the journey begin.

Are you ready?

1. Pure perfection

The way we were: Genesis 1 and 2

Once upon a time, a perfect man and a perfect woman met. After a perfect courtship, they had a perfect wedding. Their life was, of course, perfect.

One snowy, stormy Christmas Eve, this perfect couple were driving their perfect car along a winding road, when they noticed someone at the side of the road in distress. Being the perfect couple, they stopped to help. There stood Santa Claus with a huge bundle of toys. Not wanting to disappoint any children on the eve of Christmas, the perfect couple loaded Santa and his toys into their vehicle. Soon they were driving along, delivering the toys.

Unfortunately, the driving conditions deteriorated and the perfect couple and Santa Claus had an accident. Only one of them survived.

Who was the survivor?

The perfect woman survived. She's the only one who really existed in the first place. Everyone knows there is no Santa Claus and there is no such thing as a perfect man.

Women: skip on to the end of the page – that's the end of the joke.

Men: read on . . .

So, if there is no perfect man and no Santa Claus, the perfect woman must have been driving. This explains why there was an accident.

Do you ever dream about meeting the perfect man or woman? It might seem like just another fairy tale, but actually that's how God created us. We were created to relate to him perfectly, and so we were able to relate to each other perfectly. Perfect relationships between perfect men and perfect women, and all because we were created to be in perfect relationship with our Maker. That's the story of Genesis 1 and 2. Unfortunately, this 'fairy-tale' beginning takes a bit of a detour throughout the rest of the Bible . . .

So then, if the way that God created us was good and perfect, what does that perfect creation look like? What does it mean to be a man? What does it mean to be a woman? Is there any difference? Here are some students' observations concerning the similarities and differences between men and women:

Similarities

- Made in God's image.
- Flesh and bone.
- Loved by God.
- Wanting to love and be loved.
- Prone to sin and making mistakes.
- Made to be in relationship with God.
- Facing similar struggles.
- Emotional, physical and spiritual beings.
- Both face the pressure of the secular ideal of 'man' or 'woman'.
- Often one doesn't understand the other!

Differences

- Biological parts.
- Men are stronger (usually).
- Men get straight to the point; women spend hours talking about it and still don't know!
- Women smell nice; men smell.
- Women are more willing to share their emotions.
- Women usually aren't very good at reading maps, but men don't stop and ask for directions.
- Women use and understand hints or subtlety; men don't.
- Women think shoes are interesting; men think they are functional.

- Men are more logical.
- Women have different coloured pens!
- Men are task oriented; women are relationship oriented.

Meet the Designer

I often have a lot of fun presenting an eyelash curler to some poor, unsuspecting man and getting him to guess what it is for. The guesses normally range from a paper-mashing device to some sort of medieval torture instrument. The best way for him to find out what it does is to ask the person who designed it, by reading the back of the packet. Likewise, it's interesting to see what other people think of men and women and how we are made up, but the best way, surely, is to ask the Designer, who knows why we are made the way we are.

That's why the Bible, and the book of Genesis in particular, is so important to us as Christians. Genesis tells us how God created the world, why he created it, and the purpose of all the bits and bobs in it. If you want to understand what God thinks about work, Genesis is a great place to start. If you want to know how Christians should treat the natural environment, Genesis sets the foundation. If you want to discover the origin of morality, you couldn't do better than starting with Genesis. And if you want to understand what it means to be human, to be male, to be female, Genesis is the spot to begin.

> Then God said, 'Let us make man in our image, in our likeness, and let them rule over the fish of the sea and the birds of the air, over the livestock, over all the earth, and over all the creatures that move along the ground.'
>
> So God created man in his own image,
> in the image of God he created him;
> male and female he created them.
>
> God blessed them and said to them, 'Be fruitful and increase in number; fill the earth and subdue it. Rule over the fish of the sea and the birds of the air and over every living creature that moves on the ground.'
>
> Then God said, 'I give you every seed-bearing plant on the face of the whole earth and every tree that has fruit with seed in it. They will be yours for food. And to all the beasts of the earth and all the birds of the air and all the creatures that move on the ground – everything that has the breath of life in it – I give every green plant for food.' And it was so.

God saw all that he had made, and it was very good. And there was evening, and there was morning – the sixth day.
(Genesis 1:26–31)

This is the account of the heavens and the earth when they were created.

When the LORD God made the earth and the heavens – and no shrub of the field had yet appeared on the earth and no plant of the field had yet sprung up, for the LORD God had not sent rain on the earth and there was no man to work the ground, but streams came up from the earth and watered the whole surface of the ground – the LORD God formed the man from the dust of the ground and breathed into his nostrils the breath of life, and the man became a living being.

Now the LORD God had planted a garden in the east, in Eden; and there he put the man he had formed. And the LORD God made all kinds of trees grow out of the ground – trees that were pleasing to the eye and good for food. In the middle of the garden were the tree of life and the tree of the knowledge of good and evil.

A river watering the garden flowed from Eden; from there it was separated into four headwaters. The name of the first is the Pishon; it winds through the entire land of Havilah, where there is gold. (The gold of that land is good; aromatic resin and onyx are also there.) The name of the second river is the Gihon; it winds through the entire land of Cush. The name of the third river is the Tigris; it runs along the east side of Asshur. And the fourth river is the Euphrates.

The LORD God took the man and put him in the Garden of Eden to work it and take care of it. And the LORD God commanded the man, 'You are free to eat from any tree in the garden; but you must not eat from the tree of the knowledge of good and evil, for when you eat of it you will surely die.'

The LORD God said, 'It is not good for the man to be alone. I will make a helper suitable for him.'

Now the LORD God had formed out of the ground all the beasts of the field and all the birds of the air. He brought them to the man to see what he would name them; and whatever the man called each living creature, that was its name. So the man gave names to all the livestock, the birds of the air and all the beasts of the field.

But for Adam no suitable helper was found. So the LORD God caused the man to fall into a deep sleep; and while he was sleeping, he took one of the man's ribs

> and closed up the place with flesh. Then the LORD God made a woman from the rib he had taken out of the man, and he brought her to the man.
>
> The man said,
>
> 'This is now bone of my bones
> and flesh of my flesh;
> she shall be called "woman",
> for she was taken out of man.'
>
> For this reason a man will leave his father and mother and be united to his wife, and they will become one flesh.
>
> The man and his wife were both naked, and they felt no shame.
>
> (Genesis 2:4–25)

What makes us human . . .

What does it mean to be human? It's a question often talked about in the media and discussed and debated in Parliament. When does human life begin – at conception or at birth? Does someone cease to be a human when their brain needs help to function? Is there a difference between animals and humans?

Genesis gives us a beautiful description of what it means to be human. God says, 'Let us make man in *our image*' (1:26–27). The Trinitarian God says that we are made in his image, in his likeness.

He doesn't say that about any of the other things he has created. Neither the hamster, nor the monkey, nor the dolphin, nor the dodo have this seal of divine approval upon them (Genesis 1:28). Humans are different. They are placed in a league above the rest of creation because they reflect God's image. The glory of mankind is a reflected glory of the Creator. A bit like when someone sees a new baby and says, 'Oh, he's just the image of his dad.' When we look at other human beings, we should gasp in awe, for we have in us the imprint of Almighty God. Our very nature will point to the One who made us.

This is the biggest and most important similarity between men and women. We are *both* made in the image of God. This gives both men and women a humble dignity. We can take no pride in how wonderful we are, or how clever or attractive we are, because we were made by Another. But we can also have dignity and respect because each human being is made in the image of God.

Since both men *and* women are made in the image of God, that means that there is no call for the domination of one sex over the other. Just a brief glance through history, recent and not so recent, shows us times when this was exactly what happened. Women were mistreated or men were maligned. The Bible does not condone this. It says male and female are both made in the image of Father, Son and Holy Spirit, and both are made out of the same stuff (Genesis 2:23).

Part of being made in the image of God is to work. Humans were set up as God's 'middle managers' over the rest of creation and were given the job of ruling it (Genesis 1:26). Mankind was to work and serve the earth. They were to keep it and watch over it, and in doing so, they were showing that they were serving God. The work that they did indicated that they had God at the centre and that they were obeying him. They were doing what they were designed to do. That fitted them perfectly. In fact, more than that, by obeying God they were showing that they loved him. Adam and Eve expressed their love and satisfaction with God by listening to him and obeying him. And in obeying him they found full and complete satisfaction. That's what made their obedience joyful!

Differences

As we move on to Genesis 2, we zoom in from the wide-angle view of all of creation, to direct our focus on the creation story of mankind, the pinnacle of God's workmanship. We see more of what it means to be a man and a woman, to live in relationship with God and with each other. We have already seen in Genesis 1 that man and woman are created as equal. But we also see that they are different, with different roles. The word for this is *complementary* (no, not in the sense of 'Oooh, that's a lovely dress!' or 'Great strike into the top corner!'), which means that although man and woman are different, they balance and complete each other. It's a bit like two different pieces of a jigsaw puzzle: although they are different, they are of the same size and importance and fit together.

In Genesis 2 we see that Adam begins his existence independently of Eve. His role is to *work the ground* and take care of it (verse 15). Adam is also given the role of *naming* the living creatures that God created (verse 19), which shows his authority over the rest of creation. Adam's role is also to obey God's command. God commands Adam not to 'eat from the tree of the knowledge of good and evil' (verse 17). This is all before Eve shows up.

But then something happens – something shocking and startling. God declares that something in his perfect creation is 'not good': 'It is not good for the man to be alone. I will make a helper suitable for him' (verse 18). God creates Eve. He creates woman *not* because God looked at Adam and thought, 'I could do better than that, I'll have another go . . .' We've all heard countless jokes along those lines. No, it was 'not good' because Adam was incomplete on his own. Eve is made of the same stuff as Adam, but not in the same way. Adam is pretty chirpy about his other half. In fact, he's so delighted that he even sings the first love ballad about the lovely Eve (any boy-band would be proud!). You'll find his song in verse 23:

> This is now bone of my bones
>   and flesh of my flesh;
> *[key change!]*
> she shall be called 'woman',
>   for she was taken out of man.

He's thrilled really – and quite right too, for Eve is God's good gift to Adam. Did you also notice that Adam gives her a name in the song? This 'naming' shows Adam's loving responsibility for Eve and his leadership in their relationship, just as God gave Adam the instruction to give names to the rest of creation.

My dad has a mug at home which says, 'I am the boss in this household . . . and I have my wife's permission to say so' – which doesn't quite sum up the way relationships are supposed to be! Genesis tells us that woman was not made to be boss over man, neither was she made to be trampled under his feet, but rather she was created to be a *helper*.

Now, the word 'helper' isn't like when you were your teacher's helper at primary school, doing all those indispensable and vital jobs like sharpening pencils, wiping the board and counting glue-sticks. In Hebrew 'helper' is not a derogatory and demeaning term. In fact, it has a strong meaning. After all, Almighty God is referred to as Israel's helper in Exodus 18:4 and Psalm 33:20. It speaks of his strength and him fighting the battle with Israel side by side. So Adam needs Eve to help him get the job done. *Together* they can carry out the task of 'working the ground'. *Together* they can serve God and watch over the earth. Once we understand that is what God means by Eve being Adam's helper, it should fill us with joy and praise.

As well as telling us lots about how God created men and women, Genesis also tells us about sex and marriage. We hear mixed messages in the media about marriage today. On one hand, the wedding industry is at an all-time high, with the average wedding costing £20,273,[1] and yet many lobbyists send out the message that marriage is outdated and we ought to move with the times.

But in Genesis we see that marriage was created by God and was not just something that Adam and Eve invented because they thought it might be a good idea. Across the ages, across cultures and countries, marriages have taken place. Marriage is part of God's creation order, and as such it is valid for all time and all peoples. That's not to say that everyone will get married (we'll cover that in Chapter 5, 'Pure gifts'), but marriage is how God's mandate to 'Be fruitful and increase in number' (Genesis 1:28) will be fulfilled.

There's an idea!

So why did God think marriage was such a good idea? What is marriage there for? Well, the first clue is in Genesis 1: 'Be fruitful and increase in number'. This is lesson number one in the birds and the bees, folks! God invented sex! That's how we are to increase in number. That might be a bit of a shock to you, but sex is right here in the first couple of chapters of the Bible, as God declares that all in his creation is good. God says sex is good – after all, he invented it! That's so different from the common view of God as a Victorian moral killjoy.

God also tells us how to *enjoy* sex in Genesis 2:18–25. But he doesn't just give Adam and Eve the gift of sex and say 'Go for it!' He also gives them limits and guidelines – 'the Maker's instructions' for the gift of sex. Perhaps you think instructions are for wusses or for those who don't have the gumption to figure it out for themselves. The thing is, as any DIY disaster programme shows, if you don't use the instructions for your flat-pack computer table, you could very easily end up with a gerbil cage. If we don't adhere to the instructions we will use things in a way that wasn't intended. But here God shows us how sex should be used and why it should be used. It's time we reclaimed sex from *FHM* and *Sex and the City* and put it back where God intended it: within marriage and marriage alone.

Do you take this woman?

What does marriage actually mean? Is someone 'practically' married if they are living with their partner? Or what if you're engaged – does that mean you're already married in God's eyes? Right in the middle of the Adam and Eve story is this verse: 'For this reason a man will leave his father and mother and be united to his wife, and they will become one flesh' (Genesis 2:24). But Adam and Eve didn't have a mum and a dad! Therefore this verse is deliberately stuck in to teach all the generations to come. It shows us that Adam and Eve's relationship is setting a pattern of what marriage is like and what marriage is for. It's just brilliant to help us understand what marriage is all about:

Between one man and one woman

Genesis 2:24 says that a man (one man) leaves his father and mother and sticks to his wife (one wife). Three is definitely a crowd! Despite what our ever-changing society may say, marriage is between a man and a woman.

A change of relationships

The confetti, the speeches, the photos and the large hats. A wedding is a public celebration that a man is leaving his father and mother and is becoming united with his wife (likewise, of course, the woman is leaving her family and being united to her husband). It is important to have the public leaving of the family home, for both the bride and the groom, and the joining together in front of witnesses as a new family unit is formed. Now the man and woman are seen *primarily* as husband and wife rather than son and daughter.

Stick together for ever

Mr and Mrs are now united as one. They have done the leaving. Now comes the cleaving! To 'cleave' means to stick together like the super-est of glues! No unsticking. They are to stay together and stay married 'as long as they both shall live'. That makes it exclusive, too, so they are not to return to their parents, because that would be 'un-leaving'; nor are they to add others into that exclusive relationship, and so 'un-cleave'. Mr and Mrs are meant to stay together as Mr and Mrs!

One flesh

After they have publicly left their parents and joined together, they are to become 'one flesh'. That's Bible language for sex. But did you spot the order of things in Genesis 2:24? After they have been publicly joined together in marriage, they are to have sex: 'For this reason a man will leave his father and mother and be united to his wife, and [*then*] they will become one flesh.' Not before! That's strikingly different from the culture that we live in, where sex is just seen as an animal instinct or 'my need' to be fulfilled. That's not God's view of sex at all. His view of sex is much higher than that. He designed it to be used within the context of marriage. He sees the physical aspect of marriage as vitally important. He's designed it to act as the superglue to stick husband and wife together. In fact, sex is a pretty good illustration and demonstration that they are now united together in God's and the community's sight. Sex was not designed to be used outside marriage but within the ultimate security of lifelong commitment to another person. Unlike the way the world sees sex, we are not to abuse God's superglue for husbands and wives. Otherwise we will hurt each other as we stick, unstick and stick again. But much more seriously, we will displease God if we disobey him and say, 'Stuff you and your ideas!' to our Designer and Creator.

Swimming against the tide

Having a distinctively Christian mindset in the area of sex and relationships is like slamming into reverse when the rest of the world is in fourth gear. It crunches and clashes. It irritates and causes much amusement. Christians are seen as 'goody two shoes' at best and regressive fundamentalists at worst. It feels like we're swimming against the tide. It's hard work to go in completely the opposite direction to the one everyone else is going in.

While Christians long to affirm that the Bible sees men and women as made equal by God, but with differences, the world says there's no difference. So it becomes possible to say, 'It doesn't matter if I was born a man, I want to be a woman', or to declare, as some extreme feminists do, that there is no difference between men and women. Yet we can also see many instances throughout history where women have been seen as inferior and have been abused and oppressed as a result, even to the point where the murder of baby girls has been condoned.

How the world views sex and marriage is so ridiculously opposed to the Bible's teaching. It won't take you long to think of some examples. Has a friend ever said to you, 'I cannot believe you could be so naïve as to get married to someone before you've lived with them'? Or perhaps someone has said, 'How can you know if you're sexually compatible with someone if you don't actually sleep together?' A quick glance at any magazine or newspaper supplement just confirms that biblical morality is like the lesser-spotted grebe in this country. All the more reason for us to 'shine like stars' in this 'crooked and depraved generation' (Philippians 2:15). We were made to reflect God's image, and we will do that as we obey and serve him.

Questions

1. What do you think are some of the similarities between men and women?

2. What do you think are some of the differences?

3. Go through the Bible text on pages 22–25 (Genesis 1:26–31; 2:4–25). Using a different colour for each of the three headings below, highlight and discuss what the passage says about the roles and identity of
   - Mankind.
   - Men.
   - Women.

4. How does knowing you are made in the image of God make you feel?

5. How does it change your attitudes to members of the opposite sex?

6. What does Genesis 1 – 2 say about marriage and sex?

7. How does this differ from what the world/the church/you think about marriage and sex?

Note

1 According to Ask Jeeves (http://news.sky.com/skynews/Home/Sky-News_archive/Article/20080641318507).

2. Pure rebellion

Where it all went pear shaped: Genesis 3

Once upon a time a man and a woman met, fell in love, got married and lived happily ever after together. Yeah, right. When does that ever actually happen?

The way God made us, as seen in Genesis 1 and 2, seems like a fairy tale set in an ideal world and is a far cry from what we experience today. Men and women don't even understand each other, let alone get on! We have become the butt of each other's jokes.

It seems that our communication has broken down. The relationships that do exist around us are often a mess. Instead of sex being viewed as a good gift from God, it is used and abused selfishly. Even our friendships can be full of hurt and pain. It seems more like a nightmare than a fairy tale.

It only takes a passing glance at the media to see that things are the same the world over. The newspapers are filled with exposés of yet another MP's affair. For every new celebrity 'golden couple', there will be another failed celebrity marriage. Even Marge and Homer, that great bastion of wedded bliss, more often than not demonstrate miscommunication, selfishness and unfaithfulness. Domestic violence continues to be a crippling and terrifying prison for many women, while men are accused of being chauvinist pigs if they hold a door open for a woman. Families shatter and fall apart in the wake of divorce. It doesn't take long to think of examples of how relationships are far from perfect.

How did we end up here? How did we get in such a mess? It's not because of women's bad sense of direction or spatial awareness, or men's inability to ask for directions, but because of something much deeper and much more terrible. God created us to live in relationship with him and with each other. Perfectly. But something went badly wrong for all of us back in Eden.

Where it all went pear shaped (excuse the pun)
You know the basic story. Adam and Eve are merrily exploring and working in the garden (tra la la), when the serpent appears (boo, hiss). The serpent tempts

Now the serpent was more crafty than any of the wild animals the LORD God had made. He said to the woman, 'Did God really say, "You must not eat from any tree in the garden"?'

The woman said to the serpent, 'We may eat fruit from the trees in the garden, but God did say, "You must not eat fruit from the tree that is in the middle of the garden, and you must not touch it, or you will die." '

'You will not surely die,' the serpent said to the woman. 'For God knows that when you eat of it your eyes will be opened, and you will be like God, knowing good and evil.'

When the woman saw that the fruit of the tree was good for food and pleasing to the eye, and also desirable for gaining wisdom, she took some and ate it. She also gave some to her husband, who was with her, and he ate it. Then the eyes of both of them were opened, and they realised that they were naked; so they sewed fig leaves together and made coverings for themselves.

Then the man and his wife heard the sound of the LORD God as he was walking in the garden in the cool of the day, and they hid from the LORD God among the trees of the garden. But the LORD God called to the man, 'Where are you?'

He answered, 'I heard you in the garden, and I was afraid because I was naked; so I hid.'

And he said, 'Who told you that you were naked? Have you eaten from the tree from which I commanded you not to eat?'

The man said, 'The woman you put here with me – she gave me some fruit from the tree, and I ate it.'

Then the LORD God said to the woman, 'What is this you have done?'

The woman said, 'The serpent deceived me, and I ate.'

So the LORD God said to the serpent, 'Because you have done this,

'Cursed are you above all the livestock
  and all the wild animals!
You will crawl on your belly
  and you will eat dust
  all the days of your life.
And I will put enmity
  between you and the woman,
  and between your offspring and hers;
he will crush your head,
  and you will strike his heel.'

To the woman he said,

'I will greatly increase your pains in
childbearing;
with pain you will give birth to children.
Your desire will be for your husband,
and he will rule over you.'

To Adam he said, 'Because you listened to your wife and ate from the tree about which I commanded you, "You must not eat of it,"

'Cursed is the ground because of you;
through painful toil you will eat of it
all the days of your life.
It will produce thorns and thistles for you,
and you will eat the plants of the field.
By the sweat of your brow
you will eat your food
until you return to the ground,
since from it you were taken;
for dust you are
and to dust you will return.'

(Genesis 3:1–19)

Eve to disobey God and eat fruit of the forbidden tree. She then gives some to Adam and they eat it. Then they realize what they've done and go and hide from God (like that's going to work!). God confronts them and they start pointing the finger of blame (Adam blames Eve, Eve blames the serpent and the serpent doesn't have a leg to stand on). God then spells out the consequences of their actions for them and for all humankind who would follow them.

The reason this chapter is so important is that the way that Adam and Eve behaved in some ways sets a terrible pattern for us. Romans 5:12 tells us that we're all caught up and represented in the actions of Adam. The way that the serpent tempted the first man and woman to sin (i.e. disobey God) is the same as the way people are tempted today. Think for a moment about one of the things you are most tempted by. Think about how your mind works when you are tempted. See if you can spot any familiar patterns in what happened in Genesis 3.

Notice how sneaky the serpent was in verse 1.

> Now the serpent was more crafty than any of the wild animals the LORD God had made. He said to the woman, 'Did God really say, "You must not eat from any tree in the garden"?'

The serpent is Satan in disguise (see Romans 16:20). Satan himself has no power to create or to rule, so instead he works as an illusionist, a master of deception. He places doubt in the woman's mind: Did God *really* say . . . ? You can just imagine how those words were ringing round in Eve's mind. Perhaps they have rung round in yours, too. 'Surely God would *never* say something like that? That would just be stupid. I really can't believe that he would be so petty as to say that eating a little apple would be wrong. That would just be ridiculous, illogical even. He's probably just trying to stop your fun – that's a bit stingy.'

Satan is not stupid. Somehow he tries to persuade us that sin makes sense. That doing something wrong isn't wrong at all, but will feel pretty good. Sin promises something that it can never fulfil. Satan deceives us into thinking that we will be happy if we just do this one thing. He tempts us by telling us it doesn't really matter – there's no point making a big deal out of it.

His next tactic is twisting God's words: 'You must not eat from any tree in the garden' (Genesis 3:1). Sounds almost right, doesn't it? I'm sure God mentioned something about trees and not eating. But if we look back to Genesis 2:16, we see that God told Adam, 'You are free to eat from any tree in the garden; but you must not eat from the tree of the knowledge of good and evil.' What the serpent has actually done is to exaggerate and distort what God has said. In twisting God's Word, Satan is actually twisting God's character.

Whatever Satan has said has started to work. He's hooked her and is now drawing the line in. Eve enters into conversation with him. Unlike Jesus' response to temptation (Matthew 4:1–11), she doesn't rebuke Satan with God's Word on the matter and tell him to clear off. She continues chatting with Satan and in doing so starts to muddle up what God actually said. She says that God told them not even to touch the tree. D'oh! God said no such thing.

Knowing God's commands and obeying God's commands shows that we are serving him. If we don't actually know what God's will is, we won't be equipped to avoid temptation. When Satan tempts us to disobey God we will only see it for what it is if we hold everything up to the plumb line of Scripture. Don't even engage with Satan. Don't enter into a conversation with him, trying to reason with him. Get rid of temptation by counteracting it with the life-giving words of God. We'll only be able to do that if we know God's Word.

Satan then starts to pull in the line. Eve is now engaged in a conversation and Satan is subtly persuading her. He has planted the idea in her mind and already it's sounding good to her. After slighting and doubting God's character, the serpent lies: 'You will not surely die' (Genesis 3:4). God specifically said that the just punishment for disobeying his command was death. Satan denies this. It's a direct challenge to God and calls his goodness into question.

Satan is still denying God's Word today. He presents it in such a way to make me believe that I will be happier if I follow what he says. The power of temptation is the belief that giving in to it will make me happier. But the true Word of God cuts through the fog of Satan's lies and shows me that true fulfilment is found in obeying God and trusting him.

Eve falls for Satan's lies. After all, they sound pretty good to her: 'You will not surely die,' he says. 'For God knows that when you eat of it your eyes will be opened, and you will be like God, knowing good and evil.' 'Wow,' she thinks. 'I fancy a bit of that. Being like God. Why should he rule the roost, after all? I bet you that's why he told us not to eat of the tree. It wasn't for our own good. It was because God wanted to spoil our fun. He was scared that if we did eat of the tree, we'd decide what's what around here.' With that, Eve, and Adam, 'who was with her', eat the fruit (Genesis 3:6).

What did Satan tempt Adam and Eve with? Being like God. The root of sin, the strand running through every 'wrong' or 'bad' thing, is that it shows that we want to take God's place. We want to decide what's right and wrong. We want to do things our way. It's crazy really, but we – the creatures – want to seize the position of the Creator. That was Adam's sin. That was Eve's sin. That is your and my sin.

The *wagamama* principle

Another way to look at it is the '*wagamama* principle'. One of my favourite places to eat is Wagamama's Japanese noodle bar. So I got very excited one summer when I met some Japanese girls and started discussing how wonderful Japanese food was. I mentioned that Wagamama's was a regular haunt of mine. For some reason this sent them off in hysterics. I asked them what was so funny and did *wagamama* mean something dodgy? Still giggling, they brought out their little electronic dictionaries and typed it in to show me: *wagamama* means 'selfishness' – which is a rather bizarre name for a restaurant, but that hasn't really stopped me eating there!

Doesn't *wagamama* or selfishness sum up what was

going on in Genesis 3? At the root of selfishness is the ego, the big 'I'. It's all about me and looking after number one first, and stuff the rest of you. In Genesis 3, most crucially, we see the shift from God at the centre to man at the centre. They want to be like God. No longer are Adam and Eve seeking to serve God, but instead they want to serve themselves.

Consequences, consequences

The consequences of the *wagamama* principle for Adam and Eve, and for us, are far-reaching and terrible. The worst and most important consequence is the effect on our relationship with God. When we show that we want to serve ourselves rather than God, we show that we don't trust him, we don't love him and we don't believe him. God stays true to his Word and declares that we will die. He declares to Adam and Eve that, as a result of eating of the tree of the knowledge of good and evil, they are now forbidden to eat of the tree of life (Genesis 3:24).

This punishment of death is not just physical. Adam and Eve are excluded from the garden and from God's presence. That exclusion begins on earth and continues for ever. Isn't death a bit harsh? No, it's exactly right. Death is God's limit on God's creatures who attempt to be God. If I want to be God, I am a traitor and God's enemy, and so deserve death. The relationship between Creator and creature is shattered.

When we ruin our most important relationship – our relationship with God – the unavoidable consequence is that we are out of kilter in our relationships with other people too. Have you ever seen those poems in picture-frames to hang in your kitchen? There's one that says, 'If Mum ain't happy, ain't nobody happy!' If the relationship with Mum is broken, then nobody has a chance of getting along! In a much more pervasive way, our broken relationship with God is like a disease in the root which will have the inevitable consequence of affecting the branches with disease too.

Consequences for relationships

That explains why all our relationships are a mess. The root problem is that we all want to be God. We all want things our own way and so we don't put others first. As a result, we live in a world where we are both sinners and victims. We are the subject of other people's *wagamama* and we *wagamama* others. Instead of serving God and each other, we muscle our way through to look after number one first. A bit like a rugby scrum where everyone is trying to claw the ball out for themselves: they get injured by others and they hurt others too.

Its great being part of the *Friends* generation, having platonic friendships with guys and girls. Except, it's never that simple, is it? I think Harry was right to a certain extent in *When Harry Met Sally*, when he said that men and women can't be platonic friends. Let's not go that far, but the *wagamama* principle certainly makes it hard to be good friends to each other. When I want to be at the centre, it means I'll pursue friendships that fulfil *my* needs rather than wanting to serve others. A friend may flirt with me, not because he likes me and wants to pursue a relationship, but because he wants to feel good about himself. We may use friends just to give ourselves an ego boost in countless ways.

The *wagamama* principle affects romantic relationships too, whether that be marriage or going out with someone. When I want myself to be at the centre rather than God, I will want you to serve my needs. We may, therefore, try to manipulate our boyfriend or girlfriend to get what we want. We may even continue going out with someone, even when we know it's not right, just for security. My need to have that stability and someone to fall back on is more important to me than being honest with you about how I really feel. The *wagamama* principle is behind the poisonous old chestnut, 'If you really loved me, you would have sex with me.' When we push God off his throne, everything else gets messed up. The world turns into a free-for-all, with everyone straining to be at the top.

Consequences for men and women

This power struggle between people is shown in Genesis 3:16: 'Your desire will be for your husband, and he will rule over you.' Here we see the power struggle to be at the centre taken into the gender arena. The *wagamama* principle has meant that the battle of the sexes has begun. The word 'desire' is better understood when you look at its context in the next chapter about Cain and Abel: 'if you do not do what is right, sin is crouching at your door; it desires to have you, but you must master it' (Genesis 4:7). Here we see a fight for who's in charge, who is the master – sin or Cain. Likewise, in Genesis 3:16 we see a tussle for who will master who. So instead of the perfect match of Adam and Eve, like two different but equal jigsaw pieces, now the fight is on for who will come out on top in the battle of the sexes.

We see clear evidence of the battle of the sexes in society today. My main aim at school was to prove that if boys could do anything, I could do it better. From choosing maths, physics and computing at A Level to demanding that my primary school head teacher should let me do woodwork, otherwise he'd be sexist, I was determined to outdo every last one of my male classmates. The battle of the sexes has gone on for centuries – from refusing women the vote in past times to paying them less than their male counterparts in recent years. Men too are feeling the effect. For example, Fathers for Justice are campaigning for equal rights for men to see their children.

Consequences for our sex lives

None of us escapes from the effect of Genesis 3. Adam was representative of all humankind's sin (see Romans 5). We are all spoiled and affected by the fall – no matter how respectable we look. No-one escapes and no part of us escapes. Sin has affected every aspect of us. Our work is affected. Our thoughts are affected. Our bodies are affected. Our reason and logic are affected. And our sexuality is affected.

Regardless of our circumstances, or position, or name, or background, we are all sexual sinners. Whether you are single or going out with someone. Whether you have just become a Christian, or you've been a Christian for years. Whether you've never kissed someone else or whether you have. All of us are sexual sinners. All of us will struggle in this area. All of us will be tempted to listen to Satan's lies about sexual fulfilment outside of marriage. All of us will be tempted to doubt God's goodness to us.

How does the *wagamama* principle affect God's gift of sex? Remember that in Genesis 2:24 sex was the glue that God gave to bind a marriage together. Marriage between a man and a woman was the place for sex. Using the *wagamama* principle, Satan tempts us to disobey God and make up our own rules. He tells us that we'll be much happier and more satisfied if we do things our way rather than God's way.

So we are tempted to have sex outside of God's plan for it in marriage. We might be tempted to sleep around with several partners or with partners of the same sex. Or we might think that living together would be a great preparation for marriage. Or we might think and dream about having sex with someone we're not married to. Or we might be tempted to start a 'friendship' with someone who is already married because all the single men have gone. Even within marriage the *wagamama* principle means that sex can be abused and used – for example, using sex as a bargaining tool to get your own way. 'And you will be like God' is the big temptation behind every other temptation we will face.

Like looking in a broken mirror, we can see what we were created to be, yet through and through we are cracked, chipped and shattered. This perfect creation is now disfigured and stained. As a result of rejecting God as our God, we have severed our relationship with him, and this effects our relationships with each other. How utterly depressing – like the loser at the end of a game show who is told, 'This is what you could have won.' There is no hope.

Or is there?

> And I will put enmity
>   between you [serpent] and the woman,
>   and between your offspring and hers;
> he will crush your head,
>   and you will strike his heel.
> (Genesis 3:15)

God promises a 'head crusher' who will kill the serpent. If this 'head crusher' could do that, then there would be hope for a restored relationship with God. The hostility would be gone. There would be hope for a future.

Questions

1. What examples can you think of to show that the world is less than perfect in relationships?

   Read Genesis 3:1–19.

2. What are the serpent's tactics?

3. Where did Adam and Eve go wrong?

4. What are the consequences for their relationship with God?

5. What are the consequences for their relationship with each other?

6. How does the *wagamama* principle affect:
   - Relationships between men and women (generally, or friends)?
   - Relationships between boyfriends/girlfriends?
   - The gift of sex?

7. How have you seen the *wagamama* principle work itself out in your life in the area of sex and relationships?

3. Pure planets

Living in a new community as Mars and Venus: Colossians 3

Let's say a bloke named Ted asks a woman called Elaine out to the cinema. She accepts. They have a good time. A few nights later he asks her out to dinner, and again they enjoy themselves. They continue to see each other regularly, and after a while neither one of them is seeing anybody else.

And then, one evening when they're driving home, a thought occurs to Elaine, and, without really thinking, she says it aloud: 'Do you realize we've been seeing each other for exactly six months?'

And then there is silence in the car. To Elaine, it seems like a very loud silence. 'Hmm,' she thinks, 'I wonder if it bothers him that I said that. Maybe he's been feeling confined by our relationship; maybe he thinks I'm trying to push him into some kind of obligation.'

And Ted is thinking: 'Man. Six months. We started going

out in February, which was right after I had the car at the garage, which means . . . let me check the oil . . .'

And Elaine is thinking: 'But, gosh, I'm not so sure I want this kind of relationship, either. Sometimes I wish I had a little more space, so I'd have time to think about whether I really want us to keep going the way we are, moving steadily towards . . . well, what exactly? Are we heading towards marriage? children? a lifetime together? Am I ready for that commitment? Do I really even know this person?'

And Ted is thinking: 'Easy, tiger! I am well overdue for an oil change here.'

And Elaine is thinking: 'He's upset. I can see it on his face. Maybe I'm reading this wrongly. Maybe he wants more from our relationship, more intimacy, more commitment. Maybe he has sensed that I was feeling some reservations. Yes, I bet that's it. That's why he's so reluctant to say anything about his own feelings. He's afraid of being rejected.'

And Ted is thinking: 'And I'm going to have them look at the spark plugs again. I don't care what those idiots say, it's still not moving right. And they better not try to blame it on the cold weather this time. What cold weather? It's twenty-five degrees outside, and this thing is moving like a Massey Ferguson, and I paid those incompetent thieves £300.'

And Elaine is thinking: 'He's angry. And I don't blame him. I'd be angry, too. I feel so guilty, putting him through this, but I can't help the way I feel. I'm just not sure.'

And Ted is thinking: 'They'll probably say it's only a ninety-day warranty. That's exactly what they're going to say, the bandits.'

And Elaine is thinking: 'Maybe I'm just too idealistic, waiting for a knight to come riding up on his white horse, when I'm sitting right next to a perfectly good person, a person I enjoy being with, a person I truly do care about, a person who truly seems to care about me. A person who is in pain because of my self-centred, schoolgirl romantic fantasy.'

And Ted is thinking: 'Warranty? They want a warranty? I'll give them a warranty. I'll take their warranty and stick it . . .'

'Ted,' Elaine says aloud.

'What?' says Ted, startled.

'Please don't torture yourself like this,' she says, her eyes beginning to brim with tears. 'Maybe I should never have . . . I feel so . . .' She breaks down, sobbing.

'What?' says Ted.

'I'm such a fool,' Elaine sobs. 'I mean, I know there's no knight. I really know that. It's silly. There's no knight, and there's no horse.'

'There's no horse?' says Ted.

'You think I'm a fool, don't you?' Elaine says.

'No!' says Ted, glad finally to know the correct answer.

'It's just that . . . I just . . . I need some time,' Elaine says.

There is a fifteen-second pause while Ted, thinking as fast as he can, tries to come up with a safe response. Finally he finds one that he thinks might work.

'Yes,' he says.

Elaine, deeply moved, touches his hand.

'Oh, Ted, do you really feel that way?' she says.

'What way?' says Ted.

'That way about time,' says Elaine.

'Oh,' says Ted. 'Yes.'

Elaine turns to face him and gazes deeply into his eyes, causing him to become very nervous about what she might say next, especially if it involves a horse. At last she speaks.

'Thank you, Ted,' she says.

'Thank you,' says Ted.

Then he takes her home. After he has gone, she lies on her bed, a conflicted, tortured soul, and weeps until dawn – whereas when Ted gets back to his place, he opens a bag of Doritos, turns on the TV, and immediately becomes deeply involved in a repeat showing of a tennis match between two Czechs he has never heard of. A tiny voice in the far recesses of his mind tells him that something major was going on back there in the car, but he is pretty sure there is no way he would ever understand what, and so he figures it's better if he doesn't think about it. (Incidentally, this is also Ted's policy regarding world hunger.)

The next day Elaine will call her closest friend, or perhaps her two closest friends, and they will talk about this situation

> *for six straight hours. In painstaking detail, they will analyse everything she said and everything he said, going over it time and again, exploring every word, expression and gesture for nuances of meaning, considering every possible ramification. They will continue to discuss this subject, off and on, for weeks, maybe months, never reaching any definite conclusions, but never getting bored with it, either.*
>
> *Meanwhile, Ted, while playing squash one day with a mutual friend of his and Elaine's, will pause just before serving, frown, and say: 'Tim, did Elaine ever own a horse?'*

Did that sound frighteningly familiar to you? Sometimes it seems to us that men and women are from completely different planets! Perhaps John Gray is right in saying that *Men are from Mars, Women are from Venus*. Are we completely different creatures speaking completely different languages?

And yet Genesis tells us that we are not from different planets. In fact, men and women are made out of the same stuff and by the same Creator. But if we women are supposed to be bone of Adam's bones and flesh of his flesh (see Genesis 2:23), how come it sometimes feels like men are a million miles away from us in our day-to-day dealings with them?

Actually, it's all down to that old chestnut, the *wagamama* principle again. God created us perfectly.

God fashioned us to relate to and understand each other perfectly. No miscommunication. No leading each other on. No hurt feelings. Just perfect! Well, that was until Genesis 3, when things went the shape of the pear! When we put ourselves at the centre instead of God, that mucked up our relationship with him and with each other. We now see each other through those *wagamama*-tinted glasses. It means I'm always less than honest with you and you're always less than honest with me. Even with the best of intentions, my motives are tainted by my selfishness and sin. Fact. The Bible says it (see Romans 3:10–12).

Major surgery

So are we doomed to bad relationships with each other? Is miscommunication, at best, an abuse, at worst, the way it is always going to be? Bridget Jones definitely got the right idea when she burnt her self-help books in the bin! The solution to bad relationships isn't in self-help books, conflict-resolution strategies or 'how to understand the opposite sex' programmes. That's just scratching the surface of a deeper problem. Our broken relationships with each other are a symptom of a more serious disease – a broken relationship with God. The solution to restored relationships with each other must lie in the solution to restored relationship with God.

Imagine that I've gone to the doctor because I've been finding it painful to go running. The doctor assesses the problem and concludes that I've done too much road-running and I need an operation to give me new knees. But what if the doctor, instead of fitting me in for the next appointment at the hospital, just sends me home with two paracetamol for the pain? It's ridiculous to think of it, because the only solution to the pain in my knees is the drastic solution of new knees. No amount of painkillers will solve that deeper problem. Similarly, our root problem is our broken relationship with God, yet we turn to the paracetamol of self-help books instead! It's a drastic problem, it's a problem of the heart. And it calls for a drastic solution. Nothing less than heart surgery will do. For only a new heart will enable us to love God and others properly.

That drastic solution is the cross, where God, in his love, in the person of Jesus, himself bears the punishment we deserve for rebelling against him. But how does Jesus' death on the cross give us a new heart to love God as he created us to do? On the cross Jesus wasn't just stepping into humanity and sympathizing with the daily struggles we have to bear.

He was doing something much greater and more lasting. I suggest you take a moment to read Ephesians 2:11–18. Verse 15 tells us that *he* suffered the consequences of *our* failure to keep God's Word and obey him: Jesus abolished 'in his flesh the law with its commandments and regulations'. He paid the price for our failure, so we didn't have to.

And much more than that, the result is that the barrier between us and God has been removed. I was brought up in Northern Ireland in the height of the troubles. Barricades and barriers with reams of barbed wire spiralled on top were a common sight to me. They separated communities who were at odds with each other. The barriers were a massive visual symbol of the hostility between the two sides. While I was at university, the first peace agreement was announced, and I watched news footage of some of those barriers being torn down and communities being reconciled.

Unfortunately, that peace was always short-lived, but the cross of Jesus has offered an eternal resolution and reconciliation. Rather than being far away, we are now 'brought near through the blood of Christ' (Ephesians 2:13). We have that reconciled relationship with the Father. Jesus' death on the cross has destroyed the barrier (Ephesians 2:16) and has enabled us to go back to the relationship that Adam and Eve enjoyed in the garden. The wrongs have been righted. The wall has come down.

A restored relationship with God is so cosmically huge that it has a transforming impact on all our relationships. The cross removes the barriers we raise between one another, since we all recover that right relationship with God in the same way, whatever our background. Sin or me-centredness or *wagamama* has been paid for by Jesus on the cross. Ephesians 2:15 tells us that 'His purpose was to create in himself one new man out of the two, thus making peace.' Religious, cultural, status and gender-based barriers are brought down through the cross. *Wagamama* has been done and dealt with. In our restored relationship with God, we've been given new hearts to love him *and* to love and serve each other.

Jesus' death on the cross means that we are now 'one in Christ' and therefore all part of the same family. This is great news, as the cross is reversing the effects of the fall (see Genesis 3).

But what does that actually look like in practice? How can this reality make a difference in our life here and now? Colossians 3 can help us. It starts like this:

> Since, then, you have been raised with Christ, set your hearts on things above, where Christ is seated at the

> right hand of God. Set your minds on things above, not on earthly things. For you died, and your life is now hidden with Christ in God . . .
>
> Put to death, therefore, whatever belongs to your earthly nature . . . since you have taken off your old self with its practices and have put on the new self, which is being renewed in knowledge in the image of its Creator. (Colossians 3:1–10)

What not to wear

Before we were all being 'Gok Wan-ed', Trinny and Susannah were our fashion police. But God had the 'what not to wear' principle in mind long before Trinny and Susannah ever did. He says we are to take off the 'old self' and put on the 'new self' (verses 9–10). We're not to wear the clothes of the old self (verses 5–9) – instead we are to put on clothes that fit the new self. That 'new self' actually reminds us of the way God created us and designed us to be. By being in Christ we are actually being 'renewed in knowledge in the image of [our] Creator'. Jesus is bringing us back to pure perfection. Since we have been raised with him, we have become new creations with new spiritual clothes.

That's why it's important to remember who we are and whose we are: 'your life is now hidden with

Christ in God' (verse 3). One day we will 'appear with him in glory' (verse 4), but in the meantime we are to show whose we are by the life we live. We need to take off 'the old self with its practices' (verse 9), not motivated by guilt but motivated by looking back and looking forward. Looking back to the cross motivates us to live holy lives, for our old self has died (verse 3); and looking forward to the day when Christ returns to bring *his* people home (verse 4).

> Therefore, as God's chosen people, holy and dearly loved, clothe yourselves with compassion, kindness, humility, gentleness and patience. Bear with each other and forgive whatever grievances you may have against one another. Forgive as the Lord forgave you. And over all these virtues put on love, which binds them together in perfect unity. (Colossians 3:12–14)

And that's not all! Now that all Christians are part of that restored family, we are all brothers and sisters. God gives us qualities that should mark us out as members of his family. These are heart qualities that come from being part of a new humanity in Christ. This is what it looks like to be part of God's new community, God's restored people. Read once again the list of virtues in Colossians 3:12–14. What do these qualities look like in practice? What would your Christian Union look like if we lived these qualities in our relationships? These qualities mark us out as belonging to Jesus.

Keeping it in the family

Have you ever thought about Christians being brothers and sisters before? The way we actually treat each other shows to what extent we have understood that we now belong to Christ. The way you relate to your Christian brother or sister should show that you love them. It should show the watching world what it looks like to be in right relationship with God and with each other. Isn't that an amazing vision? How do you treat your brothers and sisters in Christ? Do you treat them in a loving way? Do you show compassion and patience? Do you treat them the way Christ would, or is the old *wagamama* principle rearing its ugly head?

Below are a few things some Christian guys and girls have said about how the opposite sex relates to them. Some of these things are great and are really loving. Some things are just unhelpful and don't show Christian love. True communication and loving each other as brothers and sisters in the Lord should help us overcome the whole 'Men are from Mars, Women are from Venus' problem. Have a think about these comments and see if you and your friends can add your own . . .

Hey, brother . . . (what the girls said)
Guys:

Thank you!

- Thanks for spending time with us as Christian sisters, rather than because we look good or flirt with you.
- Thank you for making sure we're included in your group conversations by not talking exclusively about one thing – e.g. football!
- When we ask for your opinion, you actually tell us what you think. Thanks for being honest!
- We really enjoy hanging out with you in a group situation rather than on a one-to-one basis. Thanks for taking the initiative in doing the hard physical work (e.g. stacking chairs at the end of a meeting).
- Thanks for walking us home at night in groups. We won't get the wrong idea and think you fancy us. It means we get home safely.
- Thanks for being protective of us in the little things, like lending us a coat when it's cold.

- You have a great sense of humour. You make us laugh and we enjoy being included in the banter!

Please don't!

- Please be gentle in the way you tell us what you think. Remember to speak the truth in love.
- Be careful with bodily contact – often girls are more affected by touch. If you keep touching us on the arm when we're chatting, we might think you like us!
- Please don't comment about another girl/a famous woman being 'really fit' – that doesn't help us as we seek to cultivate a beauty that comes from inside (1 Peter 3:4).
- We enjoy the banter, but please don't keep us going about our weight or our looks. Try not to push banter too far. (Hint: when tears start welling, it's probably best to stop there!)
- You can look at us when we are having a conversation. Please don't look over your shoulder for someone more interesting!
- We'd love you to take the initiative in clarifying 'ambiguous' relationships with girls. (Genesis 2: the man is to show loving responsibility and leadership in a marriage relationship, so why not

get into practice now?!) Chances are, if you are texting/emailing/seeing someone more than your other female friends, the girl will be reading between the lines and wondering what is going on! It would be great if you showed godly leadership and wisdom by instigating a 'chat' about where you both are.

Hey, sister . . . (what the guys said)
Girls:

Thank you!

- Thanks for taking an interest in our lives: for asking how we are and asking us questions.
- Thanks for being such faithful friends, for keeping in touch and praying for us.
- You are brilliant at encouraging us, being sensitive or showing sympathy. Thanks for your empathy.
- Thanks for being open about your feelings – it helps us to be open too.
- Thanks for not always sticking to big, girly groups and mixing with us at times.
- Thanks for being great at serving (in church/CU). You are a real example.
- We love it when you make us any manner of food or cake!

Please don't!

- Please don't flirt with us! Be careful about being too touchy-feely, or being overly 'playful'. Please don't manipulate us by playing 'vulnerable'.
- Be careful how you dress. Guys are often more turned on by sight, so it doesn't help us to live Christianly if you wear short skirts and show us your midriff or shoulders. Please don't have your bra straps on show, either. They might just be unexciting bra straps to you, but to us they're a whole different kettle of fish! We do realize our responsibility in being godly in our thoughts towards you, too.
- Be careful how you hug us – we find a side hug much more helpful for our thought lives that a full hug from the front!
- When we ask you how you are, don't just say 'I'm OK' when you're blatantly not! Guys will often just take your first answer.
- If you sign off a text or email with a 'x' or 'lots of love', we might be thinking, 'Oh, she likes me!' You might do it to everyone, but we don't know that.
- It's not that helpful when you comment about celebrity men being really gorgeous or sexy. It makes us feel inadequate.

You might think all this is a whole lot of hassle! In fact, you might think it might be simpler to ignore the other sex and just concentrate on your own, because then at least you know where they're coming from. Well, don't go in the other direction and completely avoid us for fear of miscommunicating!

Colossians tells us that we are now part of the restored community, we have been bought by Christ, he is overcoming the effects of the fall, and so we therefore need to model good, godly, healthy boy/girl relationships . . . and the only way to do that is by having a go! Don't be afraid – we have the power of the Holy Spirit and we have been given new life in Christ. We're definitely on to a winner!

The really exciting thing is that these qualities mark us out as belonging to Jesus. They scream to the watching world that we are his. The way that we relate to each other shows the world what it is like to live in a right relationship with God and will give us opportunities to tell them the good news of Jesus Christ.

Questions

1. Often we can say more with our bodies than with our lips. What examples of this can you think of in your own experience, or from TV or films?

Read Ephesians 2:11–18.

2. What effects does Jesus' death on the cross have on our relationship with God and with each other?

Read Colossians 3:1–11.

3. How is God reversing the *wagamama* principle?

Read Colossians 3:12–14.

4. Why is the 'Therefore' in verse 12 important?

5. What are the marks of being part of this restored community?

6. How can Colossians 3 help you in the way you relate to Christians of the opposite sex?

7. Think about the guys and girls in your friendship group/Christian Union/church. Do you treat each other as 'brothers and sisters with absolute purity'? For what things do you want to praise/encourage your brothers/sisters? What things would you like them to stop doing?

8. Complete your own reminder chart:

Guys		Girls	
Thank you!	Please don't...	Thank you!	Please don't...

9. How can you tell someone in a loving way that they are not treating you as a brother or sister?

10. How can you encourage or commend a fellow Christian as they show the qualities mentioned in Colossians 3:12–14?

4. Pure sex

Being sexually pure: 1 Thessalonians 4

What things make it hardest for you to live a distinctively Christian life in the area of sexuality and relationships? What are the things you struggle with in this part of your life? Perhaps some of the following things may strike home with you:

- Unhelpful thoughts
- Lust
- Homosexual attraction
- Provocative dancing at nightclubs
- Flirting
- Fancying someone who's not a Christian
- Masturbation
- Sexually explicit images in the media
- Internet pop-ups

- Internet pornography, or the availability of mobile phone downloads
- Uncertainty about how far to go with your boyfriend/girlfriend
- Pressure from a girlfriend/boyfriend to be sexually intimate
- Finding it hard to be single
- Scars left from past sexual experiences
- Fancying someone who isn't your current boyfriend/girlfriend
- Pressure from parents to get married and settle down

Some of these problems and challenges will be unique to those who are single. Some of them will be unique to those who are going out with someone. But many of them will affect you in any situation. Our sexual problems and issues are not solved by changing our circumstances. Starting going out with someone, or splitting up, or even getting married will not solve your struggles in the area of sex and relationships. Chances are, you'll swap one set of sexual problems for another! Our problem is to do with the heart, not our circumstances.

Think back to Chapter 2, 'Pure rebellion'. Genesis 3 has affected all of us. We are all fallen. This affects every area of our lives, including our sexuality. All of us will struggle to remain pure in the area of sex and relationships, whether we're single and always have been, whether we're going out with someone, whether we're on the Christian Union committee, or whether we've been happily married for fifty years. Each and every one of us will struggle with temptation, lust and dissatisfaction, because we're dealing with a problem of the heart.

In the last chapter we looked at Colossians 3 and saw that Jesus' death on the cross has dealt with the heart problem that we have. We also saw that now we're called to do a 'Trinny and Susannah' and take off the old clothes of 'sexual immorality, impurity, lust, evil desires and greed' (Colossians 3:5) and dress ourselves with clothes that are fitting for someone whose life is now hidden with Christ in God. In another of his letters the apostle Paul explains how this new life should impact the way we behave, think and act in our sex lives:

> Finally, brothers, we instructed you how to live in order to please God, as in fact you are living. Now we ask you and urge you in the Lord Jesus to do this more and more. For you know what instructions we gave you by the authority of the Lord Jesus.

> It is God's will that you should be sanctified: that you should avoid sexual immorality; that each of you should learn to control his own body in a way that is holy and honourable, not in passionate lust like the heathen, who do not know God; and that in this matter no-one should wrong his brother or take advantage of him. The Lord will punish men for all such sins, as we have already told you and warned you. For God did not call us to be impure, but to live a holy life. Therefore, he who rejects this instruction does not reject man but God, who gives you his Holy Spirit.
> (1 Thessalonians 4:1–8)

What is God's will for us? That's a question that Christians at some point or other will ask. Often we'll think of it in terms of life's big questions, like who should we marry, what degree should we study, where should we go on summer mission or who should we have in our Fantasy Football Team? This passage helps us to determine and understand what God's will is for each and every Christian. Did you spot it in verses 3 and 7? God's will is that 'you should be sanctified' (Bible jargon for becoming more and more holy and pure); he has not called you 'to be impure, but to live a holy life'. Look again at the list at the beginning of this chapter, which mentions some of the sexuality/relationship issues that Christians struggle with. How does knowing and wanting to do God's will help us in these struggles?

The holiness rule of thumb
God's will is that we should be sanctified (made pure). Is this something that is God's will for me? Is it making me more like Christ? Is it making me holy? Will it bring purity or impurity?

If we understand that it is God's will that we should be sanctified, then it works as a good rule of thumb. The Bible doesn't act like a crystal ball and give us direct answers to questions like 'Should I be thinking about her like this?' or 'Should I go out with him?' or 'How far should we go?', but it does tell us that God wants us to be made pure, and this knowledge helps us to search our thoughts and actions in the area of sex. If a particular relationship or activity doesn't or can't make me more holy, then it's not God's will. Simple as that! God has already laid that out clearly, and he's not really one to change his mind! God's will for you and for me is that we should be sanctified. So, for example, if someone says,

'I've really prayed about it and God's given me peace about sleeping with a prostitute', that's rubbish and absolute drivel! How does the holiness rule of thumb help? Is sleeping with a prostitute making me more holy? No? Well, then it's not God's will! It's kind of irrelevant what you feel about it if God has already laid it out clearly in his Word. What he says in his Word overrides our feelings and our reasoning.

Maybe a big area of struggle for you is the question of going out with someone who is not a Christian. Should I? Shouldn't I? What if they are interested in Christianity? What if all my other friends are married and I'm left on the shelf? Let's try the 'holiness rule of thumb' thing. Will going out with a non-Christian help me become more holy? How does God view people who aren't Christians? Well, the Bible says that people who have not yet trusted in Christ as their Saviour are 'dead', 'blind', 'enslaved' and 'enemies of God' (see Ephesians 2:1–3). So no matter how lovely the non-Christian is, or how foxy, or how well he or she treats you – if they do not know Christ they are God's enemy. Can someone who is God's enemy, rebelling against his will, help you to become more holy? No, of course they can't – that's completely contradictory! We'll look at this a bit more in the next chapter, but do you see how the holiness rule of thumb helps in our decision-making?

But Paul doesn't just leave us with this general principle. He goes on to spell out what it looks like in practice. I wonder – did you spot in 1 Thessalonians 4:3–8 which things are part of holy sexuality and which things aren't? The first way to be holy sexually is to . . .

Avoid sexual immorality (1 Thessalonians 4:3)
When you see the words 'sexual immorality' in the Bible, they are referring to three types of 'immorality': (1) It can mean 'fornication' – that's the old-fashioned word for an unmarried man and woman having sex. You'll find that in Colossians 3:5 and Ephesians 5:3. (2) It can also mean 'adultery' – having sexual relations with someone who is already married, or if you are already married yourself (see Exodus 20:14; Luke 16:18). And (3), it can mean homosexual practice – sex between a man and a man or a woman and a woman (see Romans 1:26–27; 1 Corinthians 6:9). God's plan for sexual activity – *all* sexual activity – is within marriage. We saw that in Chapter 1, 'Pure perfection'. Any sex other than that between a married man and woman is offensive to God, and this includes homosexual activity. If same-sex attraction is

a reality you are struggling with, then get in touch with the True Freedom Trust (see the 'Useful contacts and resources' section at the end of this book), who will put you in contact with others who share the same struggle and who are seeking to live in obedience to God. We are all to 'avoid sexual immorality'. Some of us will face particular temptations, some of us will face others, but we are all tempted to disobey God in this area. Therefore we need to have as high a view of sex as God has. Sex within marriage is something beautiful that binds a couple together and honours God. Take sex out of the context of marriage, and it becomes a means to hurt others, to seek our own *wagamama* and, most dangerously, to disobey our Creator's orders.

Did you notice that 1 Thessalonians 4:3 says, 'Avoid sexual immorality', not just 'Get as close as you can to sexual immorality without *actually* having penetration'? It says 'AVOID!!' There should be big flashing lights and sirens round that word. It means flee! Run away in the opposite direction! Don't go near it with a ten-foot bargepole! I mean, let's face it, if you're on a diet, you don't walk down the chocolate aisle in the supermarket, do you?! So if you want to *avoid* sexual immorality, should you be turning your boyfriend or girlfriend on?

That really helps us with the classic 'How far is too far?' question. Rather than wondering how much we can turn each other on 'without actually doing it', we will want to go to every length to help each other in holiness and *avoid* sexual immorality. Don't even get onto a train that you'll find hard to stop. Be honest with yourself and each other. Have that awkward conversation and decide where you will draw the line. Be ruthlessly accountable to a good Christian friend who will give you a verbal knee-capping if you step out of line and then point you to God's grace.

But we need to take seriously this command to avoid sexual immorality, even if we're not in a relationship. Does it help you to avoid sexual immorality if you're watching films that contain sex scenes or allusions to sex? Are you tempted to get pornographic downloads on your mobile? Switch your mobile off. Leave it as far away from your bed as possible. Change your greeting message to a passage from Scripture, like 'Whatever is pure . . . think about such things' (Philippians 4:8).

What about the books and magazines you read? Are they helping you to honour God and have Jesus as Lord of your thought life? Will you walk all the way round the town centre to meet your friends so that you avoid looking into the lingerie shop that your eyes are drawn to? When you're left on your own for an evening, feeling like a gooseberry, do you try to get rid of that awful lonely feeling in a way that is not honouring to God? Think about those things that cause you to stumble in this area and resolve to talk to a trusted Christian friend about them. Ask for Christ's help and grace in this area of your life.

Learn to control your body (1 Thessalonians 4:4–5)
Masturbation can be a problem for both guys and girls, whether they are in a relationship or not. That might be surprising for you. You might think you are the only person who has ever struggled with it, but in the *Relationships Revolution* research on sex and relationships among Christian students, masturbation was in the top five struggles for both guys and girls. But 1 Thessalonians 4 helps us to see that controlling our body is a way to show that we are seeking to do God's will. It makes us distinct from those who do not have the Spirit of God, who are controlled instead by lust.

We can show that Jesus, not lust, is in control of our lives, by controlling our bodies with the help of his Spirit. Our body, not just our soul, was bought at a price – the very blood of Jesus. You belong to him. Sex is not designed for one, but is meant to be used as the bonding glue in marriage. Take this command seriously and think about how you can better be in control of your own body. Take steps to break the cycle, avoid the triggers and be accountable to a trusted Christian friend.

But it's not just our bodies that we need to be in control of . . . it's also our minds. How often do we find ourselves thinking about stuff that we *know* we really ought not to be thinking about?! You might have accidentally glanced at the tabloid newspaper in the newsagent's, and now you're finding it hard to get those images out of your head. Or perhaps you've done the classic Bridget Jones thing – one minute she's just started exchanging flirty emails with Daniel Cleaver, the next minute she's daydreaming herself down the aisle with him!

The problem with thoughts is that no one else can see them. You can be the most respectable person on the outside, but you struggle with your thought life. You might never have had a boyfriend or girlfriend, or you might never have kissed your fiancé(e), and yet you struggle in your thoughts.

So how can we learn to control our thought life in order to grow in holiness? The great theologian Martin Luther once said, 'You can't stop birds landing in your hair, but you can stop them nesting there.' It's hard to stop thoughts and ideas popping into your head, but you can stop them from turning into daydreams and fantasy.

The author and Bible teacher, Peter Lewis, says we must be careful about how and what we think about other people. If we dream about people in a way that doesn't match with reality or in a way they wouldn't agree with, we are effectively committing mental rape. That might sound shocking, but we need to take sin as seriously as Jesus did. Stop thoughts from nesting in your head by memorizing Scripture and repeating it to yourself. Pray to the Lord for help – his Spirit lives in you. Then get up and go and do something useful!

Let's be radical for a moment. Let's have a think about the things we watch on DVD. Do romantic comedies actually help me to be grateful and content in all the spiritual blessings Christ has given me, or instead do they tempt me to feel bitter and resentful and to long for another person to love me? Does listening to songs filled with sexual innuendos, or even explicit sexual content, help me to remember that marriage is the only legitimate context for sex? If we take these commands in 1 Thessalonians 4 seriously, we should also think seriously about how we can grow in holiness and purity.

The final top tip from Paul, our relationships guru, is in verse 6.

Don't take advantage of your brother (1 Thessalonians 4:6)

Flirting

This is a classic case of the *wagamama* principle in practice. Flirting is all about me! Have you ever thought about why there is such a strong temptation to flirt and even randomly snog? Let's be honest and call a spade a spade – it's because we want to feel good, or in control, or we want to boost our ego. It's not helping us or anyone else to grow in holiness. Think carefully about how you act around members of the opposite sex, whether they are Christian or not. Remember, this is a way to show that we are not like the rest of the world. We are called to be different.

If you've got it, flaunt it!

Fashion, too, needs to be brought under the will of God, if we are to honour him. Girls, be careful about how you dress and why you are dressing the way you are. We are called to love our Christian brothers and not to take advantage of them.

Guys are generally very easily turned on just by

sight. Why not have a chat as a group of guys and girls, and find out what clothes your brothers in Christ are distracted by, and change or adapt the way you dress. It's hard and shopping will be a bit more hassle, but you can still be trendy (if you want!) and also God-honouring in the way you dress. Guys, you can encourage girls by commending the inner beauty and godliness of your sisters, rather than ogling and phwoarring over scantily dressed laydeees!

While guys are more turned on by sight, girls are more turned on by touch. So guys, a little warning: if you keep touching a girl on the arm when you are talking to her, then chances are, she will be wondering what is going on between you! The general rule is to think carefully about how you act with others.

Man-ipulation

Battle against the temptation to tease, flirt or manipulate. If you are in a relationship with someone, this can be a real issue. Think about how you are tempted to manipulate each other to get your own way. It may be by intentionally arousing your other half. It may be by turning on those 'little lost puppy eyes' that always get you what you want. In marriage, resist the temptation to use sex as a bargaining tool. We are called to be holy. We are called to be different. We are called to be like Christ.

Major health warning!

Sometimes God uses a carrot to motivate us to serve him. Sometimes he motivates us with a stick. Did you spot the stick in 1 Thessalonians 4:6, 8? 'The Lord will punish men for all such sins, as we have already told you and warned you . . . Therefore, he who rejects this instruction does not reject man but God, who gives you his Holy Spirit.'

If we refuse to bring our sex life under the lordship of Jesus and continue to do things our way, we're not just ignoring the wisdom of people, but far more seriously, we're rejecting God. God has graciously given us his Holy Spirit so that we can have the freedom to serve him and love him and do his will. It is God's will that we should be made holy, for in holiness true freedom and satisfaction are found.

Questions

It will be helpful if you can discuss these questions with friends of the same sex.

1. What things make it hardest for you to live a distinctively Christian life in the area of sexuality and relationships?

2. How does the holiness rule of thumb help you in these areas and situations? How might it apply specifically?

Re-read 1 Thessalonians 4:1–8.

3. What is God's will for you?

4. What is holy sexuality? What isn't it? Look up the verses below, and write down some practical ways to help you carry out God's command in each area:
   - verse 3b.
   - verses 4–5.
   - verse 6.

5. If you are going out with someone (or if you think you might go out with someone in the future!), where will you 'draw the line'? How will you help each other to avoid sexual immorality?

6. How does verse 8 challenge you?

5. Pure gifts

Making the most of your gift: 1 Corinthians 7

At the Christian festival Spring Harvest my friends and I headed off to a seminar on 'The gift of singleness'. It was just brilliant, and we all came out feeling inspired about how we could serve God in the situation we were in. Just then another friend, came by with her boyfriend in tow, planted a massive kiss on him in front of us and shouted back in triumph, 'Girls, you can keep the "gift"! You're welcome to it!'

'If singleness is a gift, how come nobody wants it?' is a fairly classic view. I was still single at twenty-seven and, to be honest, pretty content. One of my uncles couldn't quite get his head round it and was determined to play the matchmaker so that I wouldn't 'go to waste'. The conversation went as follows:

'Linda, would you go on a blind date? There's a

nice young chap in town. An architect, you know. Been to university and all. He's around thirty. He doesn't get out much, mind you.'

Hmm. Tempting. But no, thanks.

'Now, what about that man down the road? He's a farmer and he's got plenty of land. I borrow his combine harvester now and again. Good chap, now. He'd be a bit older ... about fifty-five or so, but he wants a younger wife for breeding.'

I kid you not. When I politely declined, he decided the next step was to pass me the *Scottish Farmers' Weekly* singles' page with a biro to help me along. 'Dennis the Menace (age 50) seeks his Minnie the Minx (age 25–30).' Sigh.

Does life really only start when you meet the man or woman you're going to marry? Somehow society has hung on to the romantic illusion that there is a 'perfect man' or 'perfect woman' for each of us, and then we live happily ever after (well, until the next perfect man or woman comes along). This is summed up in the film *Jerry Maguire* when Tom Cruise says to Renée Zellweger, 'You complete me.' Is 'the perfect partner to complete me' a myth or is it something that we as Christians should be searching for?

Genesis 3 taught us that we are all fallen and imperfect, inside and out. The only way we can be complete or satisfied is *not* in another fallen and imperfect human being who will let us down, but in Jesus Christ who loved us completely and rescued us utterly. Another human being cannot be my Saviour or make me complete. Think about that when you next have a conversation about your ideal man or woman. Even if a perfect man did exist, I certainly wouldn't deserve him, as I'm far from perfect myself.

Shelf life

'If there's no such thing as the perfect man/woman for me, does that mean that I'll be relegated to the shelf for ever?' There are some really dangerous and unhelpful myths surrounding singleness and marriage. See if you recognize either of these:

> 'God will wait until you're satisfied in him alone, and then he'll bring someone special into your life.'

> 'Before you can marry someone wonderful, God has to make you someone wonderful.'

Is marriage really a reward for being an extra-holy Christian? That's the assumption underlying these explanations of singleness. Or is it because God has forgotten us as, one by one, all our friends become smug-marrieds? Is God being mean and unfair?

Actually, the problem behind our discontent is a theological one – it's a problem about what we believe about God. God categorically *cannot* be mean and unfair, as it's against his nature. God is good. He cannot be anything less than good. He is good to me all the time because his character doesn't change. So if you meet someone and get to walk down the aisle in a couple of years, it's because God is so good to you. If you never have another date and die a bachelor/spinster at the age of eighty-eight, it's because God is so good to you. God doesn't promise us a husband or a wife, but he does promise us himself. We need to pray to understand God's goodness better so that we can be content in him.

The battle of the gifts

Marriage or singleness are not signs that God is extra happy with us; rather, they are gifts that he gives us to serve him. The language about gifts is taken from 1 Corinthians 7, where Paul is encouraging the Corinthian Christians to serve God in the circumstances they are in, whether married or single. He says, 'each man has his own gift from God; one has this gift, another has that' (verse 7).

Now, don't get your knickers in a twist wondering if you've got the gift of marriage or singleness. We will always be in one category or the other. We'll have one gift or the other. If you're married: congratulations. You've got the gift of marriage! If you're single: congratulations. You've got the gift of singleness! So, now it's up to you to make the most of the gift you have to serve God, because time is short (verses 29–31). Jesus is coming back, so that shapes our perspective. Do as one of my childhood TV programmes told me to do: 'Switch off the TV and do something less boring instead.'

Paul tells us that singleness has its unique benefits:

> An unmarried man is concerned about the Lord's affairs – how he can please the Lord. But a married man is concerned about the affairs of this world – how he can please his wife – and his interests are divided. An unmarried woman or virgin is concerned about the Lord's affairs: Her aim is to be devoted to the Lord in both body and spirit. But a married woman is concerned about the affairs of this world – how she can please her husband. (1 Corinthians 7:32–34)

There are lots of benefits to being single – being more free in the evenings and weekends to build friendships and serve within them, and using your time and money to serve God and his people, to name just some.

Top tips on contentment

Paul 'learned the secret of being content in any and every situation' (Philippians 4:12). Why not learn it too, using these top tips:

- Let the Bible dictate how you feel. Don't be swayed by culture or your sinful nature. As Christians, we lack nothing (see 2 Peter 1:3). God does not withhold any good thing from us – how can we feel bitter?
- Offer yourself as a living sacrifice to God (see Romans 12:1). Deliberately give yourself over to him.
- Ask for grace in time of need.
- Be thankful. Cultivate a grateful heart and be disciplined in thankfulness. Why not take a leaf out of Pollyanna's book and play the 'Glad Game'! Every time Pollyanna felt down, she'd count the things in her life she could be glad about.
- Don't feel envious or bitter. God knows best and he is good. He is always good and his character

doesn't change. He is not being any less good to you today than he was 2,000 years ago when he paid for your sin on a cross.

- Don't think of marriage as a solution for the problem of loneliness. It is not *in principle* God's solution for feeling lonely. The solution is mainly fellowship and friendship. If we're feeling lonely, we're not to look for 'another half' as a solution, but rather to develop friendships. Having this focus stops us from becoming singletons and encourages us to serve and fellowship with others.
- Remember, you are not a freak! Jesus was single, so singleness can't be a bad thing!
- Remember, you are not alone! As Christians, we are part of the church community, with brothers and sisters to love and serve, who also love and serve us.
- Work at building healthy friendships with Christian guys and girls. Don't regard every member of the opposite sex merely as a potential love interest!
- Seek accountability from a Christian friend to help deal with sexual frustration. Exercise often helps, too. To be a healthy, sexual being does not mean compromising God's moral standards.

- Talk through these issues with an older, trusted Christian friend – don't stew!
- Avoid the temptation to be inward looking. Look for opportunities to serve others.
- Get a life! Don't sit on your backside waiting for Prince or Princess Charming to come along.
- Read around the subject of singleness. Al Hsu's book *The Single Issue* is quite simply brilliant on making good use of this unique time.

I don't think anyone would ever get married if we just read 1 Corinthians 7 for our understanding of singleness and marriage! The only real reason given for marriage is that if you think you're going to 'burn with passion' (verse 9), you'd better get married! Hmm.

Thankfully, there's a lot more written in Scripture about marriage than this one chapter, including Genesis 1 and 2, which we looked at in Chapter 1, 'Pure perfection'. Marriage, too, is a gift that can be used to serve the Lord – not in the same way as a single person, but a couple can work together to serve him. The main purpose of marriage is to serve the Creator and to care for God's creation responsibly. So marriage is not fundamentally inward looking, but outward looking. Even in marriage, or when we're going out with someone, we need to avoid the temptation to be me-centred or us-centred, and instead we should focus on how we can serve God. Christians should never be cosy smug-marrieds, but people who together serve God and work for him.

Going out

The Bible doesn't talk about 'going out', but it does talk a lot about marriage. We shouldn't think about going out with someone we could never marry – we'd then have entered into that relationship for purely *wagamama* reasons. Most people do get married, so 'To be forewarned is to be forearmed'! It's sensible to think beforehand about what sort of things God says are important in choosing a 'potential life partner'. Some of these things God has laid down in Scripture as essential. Before you think about asking someone out, ask yourself the questions in the box on page 107 first.

These are the things that the Bible is definitely clear about. If God has already said it, you don't even need to pray about whether it's right or not. You don't need to wait for a special feeling or a sense of peace. He's already made himself clear. These are matters of right and wrong and we need to obey him.

Tick sheet for potential love interests

1. Is it someone of the opposite sex? (Genesis 2:24)
   - ☐ Yes. (You may proceed to the next question.)
   - ☐ No. (Say farewell – it's a No Go!)

2. Are they related to you? (Leviticus 18:6–17)
   - ☐ Yes. (Yeuch! Stop right there!)
   - ☐ No. (Brill. Please proceed.)

3. Are they already married? (Exodus 20:14)
   - ☐ Yes. (Don't even think about it. Run. Run for the hills!)
   - ☐ No. (Great. On to the last question.)

4. Are they a Christian? (1 Corinthians 7:39)
   - ☐ Yes. (Wayhey! Please consider asking them out for coffee/a walk/a dance-mat challenge!)
   - ☐ No. (Sorry. It ain't happening. Stop right there!)

Don't lose your head

I spent a little time in Kenya one summer as a student. The typical African questions went along the lines of 'What's your name?' followed closely by 'Are you married?' One lady then offered me some advice: 'Linda, never get married to a man without a head!' She wasn't talking about the possibility of a speedy elopement with a slightly odd-looking bloke I might meet in the Chamber of Horrors at Madame Tussaud's. Rather, she was referring to a passage about marriage in Ephesians 5: 'For the husband is the head of the wife as Christ is the head of the church, his body, of which he is the Saviour' (verse 23).

For a marriage to work, we need to be pulling in the same direction. Men and women need to have the same head – that is, Christ. The reason that is so important is so that a marriage can be a living, walking, talking visual illustration of Christ's relationship to the church. That might sound crazy, but I'm not making it up! Paul wrote:

> Husbands, love your wives, just as Christ loved the church and gave himself up for her to make her holy, cleansing her by the washing with water through the word, and to present her to himself as a radiant church, without stain or wrinkle or any other blemish, but holy and blameless.
> (Ephesians 5:25–27)

By looking at human marriage we should see a 'mini-me' version of Christ's marriage to his bride, the church. That's pretty exciting, isn't it? It's exciting that a Christian wife and husband, in the way they relate to each other and serve each other, can witness to the watching world about the mystery of Christ and the church. That's a crucial reason why it's so important that Christians should marry only other Christians, and therefore should only go out with fellow believers.

OK, so that bloke/girl you've got your eye on has passed your 'Tick sheet for potential love interests'. What now? Well, now it's time to use your noggin and ask some sensible questions. I'm talking about the sort of questions God would like us to ask – not just the questions that usually spring to mind, like, 'Does he play rugby?' or 'Does she look good in a catsuit?' Instead, you need to consider what marriage is for and then ask questions of yourself and your potential love interest to see if going out together or getting married would be a wise decision. I wouldn't suggest asking these questions on the first date – it might possibly put them off! But there are some things to consider before you start going out, and some which you will need to think about as you get to know each other.

The 'C questions'

Copycat questions

Remember, Christian marriage is like a mini copy of Christ and the church. What questions will help me determine if this is someone I should be considering starting a relationship with? Below are some examples, but there will be an opportunity at the end of the chapter to think up some more of your own.

- Is this someone who helps you grow in holiness?
- Is this someone who encourages you in telling your friends the gospel?
- Is this someone who will love to serve you and will want to 'present' you 'holy and blameless'?
- Is this someone with whom you can serve the Lord?
- Is this someone who will help you show to the world how Christ loves the church?
- Is this someone with whom you can focus outwards and be effective in increasing God's kingdom?

These questions are the most important questions to ask. Years down the line, there may be times when you really can't stand the sight of each other, when you're struggling with differences of opinion, or when you just don't fancy each other. Even then, if you're sure that you're more effective for the Lord's work together than apart, then that will keep you going and committed to each other. Marriage is for life, not just for the honeymoon.

Children questions

In Genesis 1, we saw that marriage is for procreation – for population, if you like! Of course, not everyone will be able to have children, and this can be very painful. We should remember that childless marriages are just as valid and valuable as those blessed with children; after all, the most important thing is the copycat question: 'Can we serve God together?' However, in most cases marriage will produce children. If this is one of the purposes of marriage, what sort of questions should we be asking? Here are some examples:

- Do we both have the same views about children?
- Am I ready and able to bring up a family?
- Would he be the type of guy to bring up a family to know God better?
- Would she make a good mum?
- How is his relationship with his parents?

Companionship questions

Think back to Genesis 2, when there was just one lonely little Adam. Well, we don't know if he was little, but we do know he was alone, and God said that was not good. Although marriage is not exclusively the place for companionship and friendship, one of the great blessings of marriage is having someone else completely united to you, who is always on your side (or should be!). Marriage is for mates! In this context we should think about questions such as these:

- Has this person shown me that they are someone I can really trust?
- Am I ready to give up my selfishness to have someone else as number one in my life? (No, not in place of God, silly. That defeats the 'copycat' purpose. D'oh!)
- Does spending time with them drain me or energize me?
- Do we always run out of stuff to talk about?
- Does our friendship exclude others, or draw them in?

Crush questions

In 1 Corinthians 7:39, Paul says a woman is free to marry 'anyone she wishes'. There are some people in this world we would wish to marry, and some we wouldn't. Thankfully, we don't all pick the same people, so it all works out quite nicely on the whole. It's the difference between a 'good mate' and a 'good maaaaate'! The Crush Factor – that tummy-turning, I-can't-eat-anything-or-I'll-vomit feeling – is pretty exciting, but the other C's need to be there too, because we can often fancy people we shouldn't be going near with a ten-foot bargepole! Questions we should be asking:

- Does the thought of them make you smile?
- Do you miss them when they're not around?
- What makes them different from other friends of the opposite sex?
- Do you grow in fondness for each other as you get to know each other?

Putting it in perspective

I was really challenged by a speaker at our Christian Union. He said, 'Would you feel short-changed by God if Jesus returned before you had the chance to get married?' In my heart of hearts, I knew that was the case. The problem was, I had too high a view of marriage and not a high enough view of serving God in the situation he'd placed me in. I don't think I was alone in that position. We all need to put marriage and singleness in the right perspective. That perspective is eternity, and in that perspective marriage and singleness are both temporary.

In Matthew 22:30 Jesus says, 'At the resurrection people will neither marry nor be given in marriage; they will be like the angels in heaven.' There will be no marriage in heaven – there will be no need for it. The population will already be at its full measure. As a married Christian, I need to see my marriage from the view of eternity. As a single Christian too, there is a marriage and a wedding feast to look forward to. Did you know that Jesus has been preparing his Bride, and continues to prepare her, to look so beautiful that she will make him gasp? She will be radiant, without stain, without spots or wrinkles. Jesus really loves his Bride, because it cost him everything to make her like that. He even washed her with his blood. He feeds her and cares for her. Did you know that's us? We, the church, are Jesus' Bride. We will all be married one day.

> Then I saw a new heaven and a new earth, for the first heaven and the first earth had passed away, and there was no longer any sea. I saw the Holy City, the new Jerusalem, coming down out of heaven from God, prepared as a bride beautifully dressed for her husband.

> And I heard a loud voice from the throne saying, 'Now the dwelling of God is with men, and he will live with them. They will be his people, and God himself will be with them and be their God. He will wipe every tear from their eyes. There will be no more death or mourning or crying or pain, for the old order of things has passed away.' (Revelation 21:1–4)

In the meantime, here are some Christian chat-up lines that you may wish to use, should the situation permit:

- Nice Bible!
- I would like to pray with you.
- You know Jesus? Me too.
- God told me to come and talk to you.
- I know a church where we could go and talk.
- Do you need help carrying your Bible? It looks heavy.
- Oh, you're cold! Ecclesiastes 4:11!
- Did it hurt when you fell from heaven?
- What are your plans for tonight? Feel like a Bible study?
- The Word says, 'Give drink to those who are thirsty, and feed the hungry.' So how about dinner?

- Do you want to come over and watch *The Ten Commandments* on TV tonight?
- Is it a sin that you stole my heart?
- Would you happen to know a Christian woman/ man I could love with all my heart and wait on, hand and foot?
- Nice bracelet. 'What Would Jesus Date?' I mean, 'Do.'
- Do you believe in divine appointment?
- Have you ever tried praying at the cinema before?
- Excuse me, I believe one of your ribs belongs to me.
- My friend told me to come and meet you. He said you're a really nice person. I think you know him. Jesus, yeah, that's his name.
- Yeah, I predicted David over Goliath.

Questions

1. Think of as many reasons as possible why it's:
   - Great to be married.
   - Great to be single.

Read 1 Corinthians 7 (see the footnote)[1] *and Ephesians 5:22–33.*

2. Now fill in the table below:

Marriage		Singleness	
Benefits	Drawbacks	Benefits	Drawbacks

3. What things stop us from enjoying the blessings of being single?

4. How can we help each other enjoy those blessings?

5. What questions should you be asking if you want to get married?
   - Copycat questions.
   - Children questions.
   - Companionship questions.
   - Crush questions.

6. What 'gift' do you have? (Are you married or single?) How are you going to make the most of the gift God has given you to serve him?

Note

1 **Understanding 1 Corinthians 7:12**. Remember that Paul is telling the Corinthian church not to try to change their circumstances but rather to remain in those circumstances, serving the Lord. He is talking about the situation where one of a married couple becomes a Christian and thinks about leaving his/her wife/husband so as to be single and serve the Lord. Paul is not condoning starting Christian/non-Christian relationships, as otherwise he'd be going back on what he says in verse 39, i.e. a widow 'is free to marry anyone she wishes, but he must belong to the Lord'.

6. Pure forgiveness

Cross-effects: Isaiah 53

Over the last few chapters of *Pure* you've probably learned that there are a lot of very bad gender gags out there. But hopefully you will also have learned many other things. You may have discovered that God actually does have quite a lot to say about sex and relationships. Perhaps you have understood what God's design for sex is. Maybe you have realized some new things about yourself too.

Here's the rub

But what if you've been challenged by some of the things that have been said? What if exposure to God's Word has caused you pain and discomfort as you have seen failure and guilt in your life? You may be wondering, What now? You see, as we submit ourselves to what God says in his Word, it will sometimes be joyful (see Psalm 119), but sometimes it will hurt – it'll cut straight to the heart. If that's the case for you, don't harden your heart and ignore it – maybe God is trying to tell you something. As a loving parent disciplines a child, so our loving Father disciplines us. A Christian can say many things, but a Christian can never truly say, 'No, Lord.' He cannot be your Lord and Master if you say you want things your way.

How has God been challenging you through his Word? Take a moment to reflect.

Perhaps you have been challenged about your attitude to the opposite sex. Perhaps you realize you've been dressing to get attention. Perhaps you've been convicted about your Internet use. Perhaps you're starting to understand that homosexual relationships are not part of God's design for us. Perhaps you realize you're hurting yourself and your boyfriend or girlfriend by turning each other on. Perhaps for the first time you've been able to tell someone about your struggle with masturbation. Perhaps you've discovered that you've made marriage an idol and are spending more time being bitter than serving God. Perhaps you know that you need to finish the relationship you're in with a non-Christian.

Perhaps you can acknowledge that you've been losing the fight in your thought life to remain pure. Perhaps you recognize that you've been living out the *wagamama* principle, with yourself at the centre, rather than God.

Back to the beginning

We shouldn't be surprised that we've been challenged and we shouldn't be surprised that we're sinful in the area of sex and relationships. In Chapter 2, 'Pure rebellion', we saw that that's exactly what God says in Genesis 3 – that each and every one of us is affected by sin and its consequences. No-one escapes.

Each one of us is 'totally depraved' – that basically means that *wagamama* has affected every part of our being. Every one of us, no matter how respectable we look, is sexually fallen in one way or another. Every one of us will be hurt and will hurt others in relationships. Every one of us will be tempted to disobey God and put ourselves at the centre. Every one of us has failed sexually. Every one of us deserves to face God's punishment for that. Each time we choose to serve ourselves rather than God, we are pushing him off the throne and are guilty of treason.

That leaves us with huge problems. The biggest one is that sexual sin, like any other sin, deserves

God's righteous anger. But it also impacts on our other relationships. Does sexual sin mean that I have spoiled God's perfect plan for me? Will any nice Christian boy want to go near me, let alone go out with me, after what I've done? How can I look at another woman without those images popping into my head? How can God use anyone so impure? Is it too late?

The good news is that Jesus' death on the cross enables us to face our past. The gospel helps us to know God's forgiveness for ourselves and frees us to be able to forgive others. You can do that because God is bigger than anything from your past; his forgiveness is more encompassing, his grace is more abundant. Sin in the area of sex and relationships does not mean you are relegated to the Nationwide Conference league of Christianity.

Dealing with guilt

Guilt and sin are a reality for all people, and different people seek to deal with it in different ways. One view is that guilt is merely psychological and just needs to be 'let go' of. One suggestion you may have heard of is to imagine a bucket of still, calm water. Think about all your worries, all the things that trouble you and the guilt that you feel. Then imagine all those thoughts transferring into a pebble you are holding. Drop that pebble into the water and watch as the ripples gradually disappear and fade away. That's supposed to represent letting go of your guilt and concerns.

Wow! All your sins dealt with in one pebble drop? All your actions which show you have put yourself at the centre rather than God – gone? Easy peasy. Just like that. It's a shame God didn't think of that, eh? Would have saved him sending Jesus to the cross. It's completely ridiculous, isn't it? To think that psychologically letting go of our sin is actually going to appease God, whom we have so utterly offended.

It is not easy for God to forgive sin. He can't just sweep it under the carpet. We minimize sin and think it's not that bad. We blame our actions on our hormones, or being tired, or the fact that we're 'just human'. We forget that the *wagamama* principle is at work behind every wrong action or thought and that we are displacing God from his rightful place as our ruler.

Or sometimes it's quite convenient for us to think of God more in our own terms than how he is described in the Bible. We reduce his holiness to our standards and think that if we're willing to overlook sin, then he is too. Compared to rapists and murderers, well, we think that God is positively lucky to have us on his side. Again, having a proper understanding that the *wagamama* principle lies behind every sin, no matter how 'small', is an antidote to this wrong kind of thinking. Each time we disobey God shows that we want to be like God and make up the standards. He is right to be angry at our rebellion.

Cheap forgiveness is not an option for God. He is rightly angry at us, and our only hope must lie in removing that anger from us. And we are helpless to do that. *Wagamama* has affected every part of us. We cannot make ourselves right before God. We cannot plead or work our way back into relationship with him. The drastic and complete solution that God offers – the *only* solution that God offers – is the cross.

How does Jesus' death on the cross help us work through past sexual sin? How can it help when memories of the past haunt us and cripple us today? We looked at the cross in Chapter 3, 'Pure planets', but to help us understand how the cross deals with the guilt of sexual and relational sin, we need to look at how the cross is God's answer to the entire problem of human sin. Why did Jesus have to die?

My friend will pay

Let's go back, way back. Back to the Old Testament, where we read about a promised Rescuer in Isaiah 53.

(Hint: it's talking about Jesus, and if you don't believe me, see how the New Testament applies these verses to Jesus: Acts 8:26–40; 1 Peter 2:22; Philippians 2:5–11.) Isaiah has already talked about the bad news – God's people have rebelled against him and they're in trouble. Now for the good news – God's Servant would sort it out. Cue *Mission Impossible* music.

The Rescuer who is prophesied in Isaiah 53 was an unlikely candidate. Pretty gross, actually. He's disfigured and gruesome. Some of my medic friends used to delight in telling me stories of blood and gore from the operating theatre (usually over dinner). But if something is really grotesque, our automatic reaction is not to look at it but to turn our face away:

> Just as there were many who were appalled at him –
> his appearance was so disfigured beyond that of any man
> and his form marred beyond human likeness . . .
> Like one from whom men hide their faces
> he was despised, and we esteemed him not.
> (Isaiah 52:14; 53:3)

This Servant carried such suffering and agony in his being, that it repelled and repulsed people. And as any Old Testament person worth his salt would know, someone suffering such agony was seen to be under the wrath of God. What did he do to deserve it?

> But he was pierced for our transgressions,
> he was crushed for our iniquities;
> the punishment that brought us peace was upon him,
> and by his wounds we are healed.
> We all, like sheep, have gone astray,
> each one of us has turned to his own way;
> and the LORD has laid on him
> the iniquity of us all.
> (Isaiah 53:5–6)

It wasn't karma on the Servant, or plain old bad luck. The agony of the Servant wasn't caused by fate or chance, but God himself was inflicting the suffering on him. The reason is found in verse 5. The Servant was suffering and was rejected for the sake of someone else. Jesus was dying in place of someone else: '*he* was pierced for *our* transgressions'. There was an incredible exchange going on. The Servant was taking the punishment *we* deserved upon *himself*.

My friend, Helen, is just brilliant. She periodically sends me vouchers for clothes or groceries or DIY bits and bobs. When I've picked out what I want, I take it to the till and hand over the voucher to show that my friend has paid already. I don't have to pay for it again. It is paid in full.

In a much more amazing way, Jesus (the Servant) pays up what we owe to God. He pays so we don't have to. Perhaps you have seen the *Friends* episode when Joey and Ross get to go around in a police car in the rough part of town. A gunshot goes off (well, it emerges that a car backfired!) and Joey leaps across the car to protect his friend Ross from the bullet. Ross is so grateful throughout the programme because Joey would have given his life so that Ross could live. Unfortunately Joey was actually just protecting his meatball sandwich.

At the cross, Jesus takes upon himself the full brunt of God's anger, and it's diverted away from us. He experiences its full force instead. God's anger is satisfied and used up, and we can be forgiven.

Jesus' death as the Servant achieves God's will (Isaiah 53:10a). Through it, many people will be declared right before God (verse 11b). It has provided the way for a restored relationship with a holy God (verse 12b). How brilliant!

Do you think, when Jesus was hanging on the cross for 'the iniquity of us all' (verse 6) and bearing 'the sin of many' (verse 12), that he meant all sins . . . *apart* from lust? Do you think that Jesus only died and paid for 'decent' sins? Was there some sort of exclusion clause saying, 'Those who have sinned sexually need not apply here'? Of course not! When Jesus died, he died for all sins: hidden and outward, lies and deceit, sexual sin and pride.

Think about that for a moment. What are you most ashamed of? Think about your deepest, darkest sin. Now realize the impact of Christ's completed work on the cross. If you are trusting in Jesus' death as your only hope before a holy God, *all* your sins have been nailed to the cross and paid for with blood. *That* sin is nailed to the cross. *That* sin sent Jesus to the cross, but now he has paid for it so you could be declared pure. His love is not half-hearted. His death was not deficient. His achievement was complete.

And to prove it, God raised Jesus from the dead. A good job, well done. Isaiah says that the Servant will be 'raised and lifted up and highly exalted' (Isaiah 52:13) and that 'After the suffering of his soul, he will see the light of life and be satisfied' (53:11). Jesus' death and resurrection show that he has defeated death and sin and that God's people really are forgiven. That gives us great confidence in the future. When we face God on the final day, we can say, 'My friend has paid.' We can have absolute confidence when we look at the resurrection. It declares to the world that Jesus was justified. He has been shown to be blameless by God raising him from the dead. Like being identified with a big brother, we too can claim the benefits of Jesus' resurrection. We too will be raised to life again and will live in relationship with God for ever. It's an awesome future to look forward to.

But the benefits of the resurrection aren't just in the future – it also affects us in the present. It brings us assurance that our sins have been dealt with. Jesus didn't stay dead, but rose again, proving his victory over sin. Satan may accuse us of our guilt, but when we look at the empty cross we know that Jesus paid for it all. There is nothing left to pay. God's wrath is satisfied, and we can be satisfied with that.

So if you have asked God for forgiveness for that sin and have turned around to trust in him, you are without blame. It's as if you hadn't done it. God sees you as utterly pure because of the Great Exchange at the cross. So when the past comes knocking and you feel like a second-class Christian, you can say with confidence and assurance, 'Oi, Satan – no!'

> He himself bore our sins in his body on the tree, so that we might die to sins and live for righteousness; by his wounds you have been healed.
> (1 Peter 2:24)

You gotta have faith

How, then, should we live as a result of Jesus' death on the cross? Romans 3:25 tells us that Jesus' sacrifice becomes effective 'through faith in his blood'. Forgiveness from guilt is only possible through faith. That doesn't mean leaving your brain at the door and believing in something impossible. Faith isn't something you're born with and you either have or don't have, like red hair. Faith means 'trust'.

When I was travelling around New Zealand with a friend, I decided to do a bungee jump. Max said she had faith that the rope would hold her weight, as did I. The difference was that I did the jump and she didn't. If I truly trust in something I'll show it by my actions. My actions showed that I had faith that the rope wouldn't snap. Likewise, we can trust that Jesus' death on the cross did 'exactly what it said on the tin', and we can accept the forgiveness by faith. Or we can reject it as untrue and face the consequences of our guilt before a holy God.

If you are trusting in Jesus' sacrificial death as the only way to be restored to a right relationship with God, you will experience real joy. When Satan accuses you of being a 'fake Christian' because of what you have done in the past, this can be your testimony:

When Satan tempts me to despair
And tells me of the guilt within,
Upward I look and see Him there
Who made an end of all my sin.
Because the sinless Saviour died
My sinful soul is counted free,
For God the just was satisfied
To look on Him and pardon me.

What should you do when the past comes knocking? Will you let yourself wallow or will you speak truth to yourself? Go back to the cross. Look how Jesus paid for your sin. Look to the resurrection. Jesus rose again to show that it was paid for. You are free.

No boasting here

The cross also means that there is no room for boasting or pride (Romans 3:27–28). The cross was an extreme and only solution to your sin. Don't kid yourself into thinking that you're good enough for God on your own. We need to abandon confidence in our own achievements, for in God's eyes they're like scrappy little bits of rubbish. It's like offering an old, manky bit of chewing gum as a payment to go and live with the Queen. The cost is too high for any of us to pay, so don't boast that you can. The cross is our only hope for acceptance.

Most of us aren't as blatant as that. We do 'boasting' in a much more subtle way. Are you ever surprised when you sin? Do you ever find yourself saying, 'I can't believe I did that'? Perhaps you struggle with a particular sin time and time again. Do you find yourself saying, 'I'm so stupid! I need to do better next time'? It's as if we're surprised that we are sinners, and so we self-righteously tell ourselves to try harder not to sin.

The cross tells us that is not the cure! The cross leaves no room for boasting. We shouldn't be surprised at our sin. The right response is not 'I'm better than this, I need to try harder', but to turn in our weakness to Christ who forgives. Don't come out with 'holy' drivel like 'God might be able to forgive me but I can't forgive myself', or wallow in self-pity to punish yourself. Jesus has taken God's complete and full punishment upon himself. Please don't think you can top up what Jesus did on the cross. The only solution to pride is a humble acceptance of what Jesus has done for you.

A new lease of life

We can live as those who have been brought from death to life: 'I have been crucified with Christ and I no longer live, but Christ lives in me. The life I live in the body, I live by faith in the Son of God, who loved me and gave himself for me' (Galatians 2:20). The great news is that the old life has gone. Jesus has done a Trinny and Susannah and got rid of our old clothes stained by sin, and now we are clothed with him.

This is a fact that gives us much freedom. Perhaps you've been struggling with sexual sin from the past. You've repeatedly come before the Lord for forgiveness but still feel the shame and guilt from it. But the message of the cross is that the old self and all its 'accessories' are dead and gone. How can you continue to feel guilty about something that's no longer associated with you? Praise God and look to the cross where the Saviour 'made an end of all my sin'.

How do we forgive others who have hurt us in the past? How do we deal in a godly way with a boyfriend or girlfriend who has been sexually active in the past? This is definitely a difficult subject and it is right to feel upset by the loss of something precious. It is important to grieve. But the cross will not let us stop there and reminds us that we are all sexual sinners in one way or another. You have a wonderful opportunity to be a channel of God's grace to others. If God has forgiven them and sees them as pure in his sight, we too must pray for his grace to treat them as such.

Spirit led

The message of the cross also urges us to be led by the Spirit. This side of heaven, we will always struggle with sin, and yet we're not in a losing battle. In fact Romans 8:9–14 tells us that we now have the Spirit of God. Ownership of us has changed hands, from the sinful nature and the *wagamama* principle to the Spirit of Christ. We need to be controlled by the Spirit, not the sinful nature. We are no longer slaves to sin. We don't have to sin. We have to fight and keep in step with what the Spirit wants us to do. That's what we've been looking at through the whole of this book.

We've looked at the many temptations and struggles we all face in the area of sex and relationships. When we are tempted to be controlled by the sinful nature rather than by God's Spirit, we need to remember the cross and resurrection of Jesus. Sin was nailed to the cross. It has no hold over us any more. Jesus defeated death, giving us an assurance of forgiveness. We belong to Christ. We have the freedom to live in relationship with God, serving him and each other, just like back in the good old days of Eden. Except better, much better. Now we know the price that was paid for us to be in that position. Praise God!

Shine like stars

> Do everything without complaining or arguing, so that you may become blameless and pure, children of God without fault in a crooked and depraved generation, in which you shine like stars in the universe as you hold out the word of life . . .
> (Philippians 2:14–16)

In the midst of today's sex-obsessed society, living the pure life that God calls us to may feel more like sticking out like a sore thumb than shining like stars in the universe. It will be hard work. We will fail at times. We will be ridiculed and mocked. We will suffer from outside and within. But we have a great hope to keep us going: hope of an eternity being married to Christ and giving glory to God.

My prayer for us – for all of us – is that we would live a distinctive and pure life that will cry out to the world around us that the message of Christianity is true. I pray that our lifestyles will make the great news of the gospel attractive to those who do not know Jesus. And I pray that each of us will hold out the word of life – telling the lost how they can be found in God, telling the hopeless that there is hope in Christ, and telling the guilty how they can go free.

Questions

1. What things have you been challenged about as you have read *Pure*?

2. How have you tried to make yourself feel better about past failure and sin?

3. Why hasn't that worked?

Read Isaiah 52:13 – 53:12.

4. How could the holy God accept an unholy people?

5. Have you taken part in the Great Exchange?

6. How does the fact that Jesus has paid the punishment for your sin affect your life:
   - in dealing with your past sins?
   - in dealing with others' sins?
   - in dealing with your present struggle with sin?

7. What steps will you take to put *Pure* into practice?

8. How could you use the following questions from non-Christian friends as an opportunity to 'hold out the word of life' and explain the gospel?
   - 'Why don't you sleep with your boy/girlfriend?'
   - 'I can't believe you're still single! Why aren't you going out with anyone?'
   - 'Why won't you go out with a non-Christian?'
   - 'Why don't you have any *FHM* posters on your wall? They look a bit empty.'
   - 'I really like the way we're just friends and you don't flirt with me and lead me on like other girls/boys. Why is that?'

Afterword

Having gone to church with my family for as long as I can remember, I gave my life to Christ when I was eighteen. I attended a great church, and felt really passionate about the Lord and his Word. It's only looking back now that I realize that there was a huge part of my life which I had not submitted to Jesus. There was an ever-present blind spot in my faith, a side of me which was not affected by my new life in Christ. It seems absurd now, but it never occurred to me that in my relationships or encounters with men, as in everything else, I should be obedient to the Lord.

The first experience I had of the *Pure* course was in my first year at university. It's a testimony to my lack of concern about sex and relationships issues that I only made it to the final session – 'Pure forgiveness' –

and this almost by accident. This session really turned my life upside down. I remember one person asking advice on how to cope if a boyfriend/girlfriend has made big mistakes in the past – for example, having 'kissed lots of random people'. I remember hearing this and realizing that it applied to me. I suddenly felt completely convicted. After thinking that I had nothing to regret in this area, I now saw that *my* past might be difficult for a future boyfriend to cope with. In short, I realized that I had sinned in this area a *lot*. Other issues were raised, such as why it isn't good to go out with a non-Christian. This was something I had heard of, but to me it had seemed judgmental.

After the shock of this encounter with *Pure*, I slowly began to learn that God wanted me to be holy in this area. I struggled with many things, such as my feelings for non-Christian men. The conviction that 'pulling' people was not godly required huge adjustments for me. My social life at home had been based around getting drunk and finding nice men to kiss. The hardest thing was finding the courage to convey to my friends that I did not want to do it any more, and trying to tell them without sounding judgmental.

The following year, when the *Pure* course started again, I was thirsty for wisdom about relationships. By then I was a small-group leader, and I dragged members of my group along with me, determined that they too should hear this teaching. I did not want them to have the stunted Christian growth that I had suffered from.

The first two weeks of *Pure* were amazing. Learning that God had created men and women to be different, and that this was to be celebrated, was really liberating. Even more helpful was the discovery that the awful confusions between men and women were a result of the fall of humanity. Finally I knew why issues with men could be so complicated and painful. Understanding the reason does not take the pain away, but it has certainly helped me to pray about it and to do my best to reverse the process.

As the course continued, the practical advice about how to love our brothers, and also how to avoid temptation, was immensely helpful to me. Shortly after attending the course in full, I entered into a relationship with a Christian man. I remember feeling very grateful for advice from the course which had seemed a little strange when I had first heard it: 'Never underestimate how sinful you are.' Steering clear of danger is so much more important in relationships than I had realized.

For many people who become Christians, as with myself, the area of sex and relationships in their lives is one of the last to be addressed. Because of God's Word, I now realize that the opposite should be the case. Our culture is increasingly dominated by sex, and as new creations it is important for the sake of the lost that we are distinctive. Not only that, but it is also absolutely crucial that we release the power of God in this area before the devil gets a foothold. Only now, as I continue to allow God to heal my wounds, do I realize how damaging my sinfulness has been. I thank the Lord that he brought me to the *Pure* course, where I learned how to begin to live a life worthy of the calling which I have received in Christ Jesus.

Catherine Brooks (aged 22)

Useful contacts and resources

Boy Meets Girl by Joshua Harris (Multnomah). Looking specifically at the issue of 'going out'.

Captured by a Better Vision by Tim Chester (IVP). Tim exposes the lies and deceptions of porn, inviting us to be fully free, and sharing positively and practically how this can be possible in daily life.

God, Sex and Marriage by John Richardson (Matthias Media). A closer look at 1 Corinthians 7.

Relationships Revolution by Nigel Pollock (IVP). A general book about relationships.

True *freedom* Trust, www.truefreedomtrust.co.uk
True *freedom* Trust is an organization set up by

Martin Hallett, a man who faces the reality of same-sex attraction. T*f*T seeks to support men and women who face same-sex attraction and want to live a life that is in line with biblical teaching. T*f*T also provides teaching materials for individuals and churches, seeking to facilitate greater understanding and a compassionate response within the evangelical church.

If you would like to run *Pure* as a course, subscribe online for downloadable session plans, PowerPoint presentations, handouts and more at www.ivpbooks.co.uk/pure.

pure

Sex and relationships God's way

Linda Marshall

ivp

The disciples had seen an age that the prophets and kings had longed to see (Luke 10:23–24). The new age was here (Matthew 11:2-6; Luke 7:18–23).

Where Jesus went, the kingdom broke out, in all of his words and works. Demons were being driven out, sure evidence of a clash of invisible kingdoms. The territory of the false king-pretender, Satan, was being pushed back, as like a relentless avalanche the rule of Christ rolled out with a thunderous roar.

The kingdom – it's all about *you,* Jesus

The kingdom has never been about a distant monarch or impersonal rules and regulations – as we saw in the last chapter. Rather, the kingdom of God was present for people whenever Jesus was present. As he walked and worked, the kingdom came (Luke 11:20). The religious leaders of the day made the same mistake that we are tempted to walk into – they were looking for other "stuff" and signs to announce the kingdom's arrival, but failed to spot the king among them. We can do the same, as we get over-enamoured of the signs of the kingdom – the gifts of the Holy Spirit, healing, deliverance – wonderful and vital though all these are, or when we reduce our Christianity to an impersonal moralism, a Christless Christianity that knows how to be good but knows little of the touch and a whisper of God.

Kingdom RSVP

Unlike the warrior human kingdoms, where the rule of kings and queens is extended through bombs and bullets, the kingdom of God comes as it is received. It is at hand – it is within the grasp of all who see the demonstration and hear the proclamation, and there are many who today are "not far from the kingdom" (Mark 12:34). As we respond willingly to the invitation, we are invited to step into the banquet life now.

Nothing is more important than our response to the kingdom rule of God. It should be our first priority of business in life, item number one on every agenda (Matthew 6:33). As we humble ourselves, we become part of it (Matthew 18:1–4).

But what about the church?

The church is *not* the kingdom of God. This is not just a theological detail but a vital fact: when we confuse the church with the kingdom, we get the idea that God only works in the realm of the church, cut off from the real world, and only acts in the cloisters of the church – a tragic misunderstanding.

As we've seen, the kingdom of God is the sphere of the dynamic rule and reign of God. But the church is only the *primary agent* of the kingdom. God extends his kingdom in all kinds of ways. He will, at times, directly intervene in people's lives; he whispers and shouts through creation. But the main way that he has chosen to extend the kingdom is through a visible, working model of kingdom life: his church.

Sometimes the model works well – and sometimes it's a hideously damaged array of grinding, clashing cogs and wheels that is the worst possible advertisement for the Good King. So, as we live and announce that there is a new rule to live under, that we are now subjects of another master, so we have the ability to draw others to kneel at the throne of love – or perhaps run from it, if our demonstration is bad. In this way, the church holds the keys of the kingdom (Matthew 16:19; 18:18) and carries the awesome responsibility of opening and shutting the kingdom to others. The breathtaking truth is that as you and I go about life, we are carriers of the kingdom – and represent it either well or badly. When the disciples travelled from town to town, those who encountered them came near to the kingdom of God (Luke 10:8–12). Again, this is more than theological musing. All of us – without exception – carry *influence.* The way that we use it in our day-to-day lives will affect the way others view both us and the kingdom we represent. We can leave impressions that last a long, long time – even eternally, either for good or for evil. We are not only influencing others in the formation of their opinions about us, which, let's face it, are not that important, but also in their opinions about the effectiveness of the Great King. They will judge *him* as they look at *us.*

Just as Israel was called to be "light to the nations", so

the church is designed to be the visible expression of what it means to live under a new rule – the reign and authority of God. When we become part of the kingdom, we discover a new community of fellow subjects, and so entrance into the kingdom means participation in the church.

And that will be costly, because we (the church) are on the journey but know the painful truth that we have not arrived yet. We should therefore never be surprised at the imperfection of the church. Just as we have not yet breasted the winner's tape, neither has she. Just as the kingdom is both "now" and "not yet", so is the church. She belongs to two ages. She lives in the current age of sin and destruction, but she also belongs to the age to come – of better things ahead. And she is called to model this truth through humility, mercy, and forgiveness (Matthew 7:1–5). It is the duty of the church to display a shop window of the future. In an evil age of self-seeking, pride, and animosity, she lives out the life and fellowship of the kingdom of God and the age to come. So "kingdom living" is an essential part of the witness of the church – she is not just a *proclaiming* community, but in her lifestyle is a *demonstrating* community.

Let your kingdom come: how will our prayers be answered?

As we draw this brief look at the kingdom to a close, we must ask, as we pray, "Let your kingdom come": how will that happen?

The kingdom breaks out as the message of the gospel is clearly announced. The gospel of the kingdom – the wonderful news that through the death and resurrection of Jesus, the power of the enemy has been broken, and we can experience freedom as we receive the message – this is the church's message. We call people to come in repentance – the number one requirement for entering the kingdom – to the king himself, whose rule is open to anyone who lays down their rebellion. We call people not just to pray a sinner's prayer, but to hand over – to lose – their whole lives, in order to place those lives under new lordship (Mark 8:35). This is not just insurance for life after death, but an invitation to experience kingdom life before death, here and now.

And then we are called to demonstrate the power of the kingdom. Jesus operated through both proclamation – announcing the good news – and demonstration: healing the sick and casting out demons. The disciples carried out the same dual role of healing and deliverance – they too cast out demons and healed the sick (Matthew 10:8; Luke 10:17). Their power was delegated, yet they operated in the very same power that had worked through Jesus. So the conflict between the "gates of hell" and the kingdom of God will continue through the ministry of the church in the same way as it did in the life of Jesus.

This demonstration will not only be in the supernatural. As we echo God's heart for social justice, we begin to express the values of the kingdom, as the poor, the oppressed, and the downtrodden suddenly find themselves blessed in Jesus' new order of things. We must hold unswervingly to this kingdom message. As it is preached and modelled across the earth, "then the end will come" (Matthew 24:14).

And all this means… what?

As we pray, "Your kingdom come", we immediately bump into a few important realities. First, we realize what the church is actually for. Contrary to our consumerist ideas, the church is not here for me at all – it is here for the release of the kingdom. Our obsessions about whether we like the music/the colour they have painted the church's kitchen/the preaching style/the brand of tea bags we use fade into irrelevance (except that the tea needs to be Fairtrade!). The church is not here to serve us or particularly please us. It is here to serve the king and his purposes. And then our church programme or structure is not of the highest importance. The issue really is what programme or structure will serve the purposes of the kingdom. We pray for a kingdom mentality towards change in the church. We are not addicted to change for the sake of it, but fully open to change so that the kingdom is strengthened and extended.

Understanding the gospel of the kingdom will prevent us from being tempted to simply lock people up in church activity; we will want to release them to be part of those who fulfil their call to seek first the kingdom of God, in whatever sphere they find themselves. More about this in the next chapter.

The truth of the kingdom helps us avoid parochial praying for our church. Indeed, our primary prayer is not for the blessing of one church or indeed all the churches in the area, but rather that *the kingdom might come.* And understanding something of the clashes between the kingdoms of light and darkness gives us a focus for spiritual warfare.

The kingdom teaches us to be patient in prayer – and fellowship. We are already aware that we live with a tension of the "already but not yet", and so we live knowing that the actual is not the ideal. We work with the actual but do not let go of the ideal – we are neither pessimists nor unrealistic.

We do not look for the restructuring of society along a "biblical model", as have some – our kingdom is not of this world – but we do look to be "salt and light" within society, transforming our environment as the goodness of God's kingdom touches lives.

The kingdom becomes our priority. Let it come.

> The church gets into trouble whenever it thinks it is in the church business rather than the kingdom business. In the church business people are concerned with church activities, religious behaviour and spiritual things. In the kingdom business, people are concerned with kingdom activities, all human behaviour and everything which God has made, visible and invisible. Church people think how to get people into the church, kingdom people think about how to get the church

into the world. Church people worry that the world might change the church, kingdom people work to see the church change the world.[28]

28 Howard Snyder, *Liberating the Church*, Eugene: Wipf & Stock, 1996.

Prayer: it is about us

"Give us today our daily bread."

We've established that the ever-tempting spirit of selfishness shouldn't hijack our prayers. But if you stop reading this book now, you'll cower away from the possibility that you could pray about your own life and all the everyday details that make your life what it is. And you'd be wrong. Jesus, having given us the priority of the kingdom, invites us to share our daily needs, worries, and indeed all of the assorted paraphernalia that makes up your today. He is the God who has decided to be interested.

God *is* interested

The thought slammed into my head: why on earth does God seem to view prayer – us talking with him – as so important? What's the big significance about us having what often seems like a one-way conversation? Is God lonely, and in need of company? Perhaps our hurried answer to that question would be *no.* We rush to consider the God who is without need, who is surrounded by the glories of angelic courts, and who lives, as one writer puts it, "a very interesting life" in his interaction with creation. I do believe, however, that as the core fabric of God's identity is love, there *is* a sense in which he longs for us and for our friendship. I hesitate to say this. Some preachers have portrayed the Jesus who stands at the door and knocks as some kind of poor chap out in the cold, desperate to be let in. It's a picture I reject, as a distortion of the biblical portrayal of Christ at the door. And yet to love is to deliberately make yourself vulnerable and in need of the one that you love. A friend of mine shared how he had gone through an extended time of spiritual barrenness when he had found little time for prayer. His testimony was that when he returned to God, the Lord whispered, "I missed you."

God is interested in us and in everything about our little lives. It's important to remind ourselves of this, lest we begin to see prayer as a spiritual activity that needs to be done, well, simply because it needs to be done, a bit like the spiritual equivalent of brushing our teeth twice daily. When we treat prayer like this, it becomes a task without purpose, except that we feel that we have "done the Christian thing" by engaging in it. The beautiful news is that in a world where we can feel lost in the crowd, a mere digit in the great, overflowing database called Earth, there is One who wants to listen to us with genuinely avid interest. We've all known the disappointment of sharing something sensitive and deep with another, only to watch their eyes glaze over as their available quota of interest in us has apparently run out. Yet we, without pompous self-absorption, all want to be known and heard. There is something wonderful about the ability within a vintage friendship to be able to take the lid off the confused inner space inside our heads and peer inside, hand in hand with that friend. God is interested: there will never be a yawn from him when you pray; the Amen to conclude the prayer will always come from you. And his interest is not to be reduced to forensic information-gathering. Rather, he desires to entwine himself into the warp and woof of our daily lives.

Request and conversation

Allow me gently to look at an area that gives me some concern – the idea that prayer is designed to be a two-way conversation, a dialogue with God. I worry lest we end up disappointed that we don't have this dynamic interactive encounter going every day – and we assume that everybody does, and therefore we should. Let me say immediately that I know God wants to speak to us. As we read Scripture and meditate upon it, as we walk the dog, work at the office, listen to the prophets, hear the preacher, the voice of God is there to be discerned and heard. And of course, the whisper of God can be found directly in times of prayer. I'm just not convinced that prayer is designed to be some fluid, flowing conversation between us and him. The few people I've known who confess to these constant "I said and then God said" matey chats as their experience have, quite frankly, worried me. I have even wondered about the robustness of their mental health. As I look at the Lord's Prayer, it seems to me that it is primarily about what is really a one-way conversation: us coming to God and leaving our worship, our fears, our sins, and our requests with him. What delight comes when we sense his immediate response; yet we should not feel rejected if we come, we speak, and that's it. I've no doubt we would hear more if we would be still more, and there are some understandable and unfathomable reasons for our not being able to discern more of his voice. Yet we can come, pray, and know we are heard, whether or not we feel the psychological comfort of an immediate response.

God bless me

A few years ago, *The Prayer of Jabez* became a publishing phenomenon. Millions of copies have been shifted, and the attractively presented little book by Bruce Wilkinson has spawned a whole family of merchandising spin-offs.

The concept is simple: an encouragement to ask God to bless *me*. And what's so very wrong with that idea? We are quite wrong when we refuse to ask God to do anything for us at all. We touched on this earlier, but let's consider it again: perhaps most of us struggle with the idea that God might want to bless *us*. Of course, he wants to heap gifts on dear old Mrs Bloggs who has baked cakes to raise money for the missionaries every Friday for the last 300 years, and God *definitely* wants to issue heavenly credits to Mr Whatsisname, who faithfully and without complaint sweeps up the cigarette ends around the back of the youth hall. We wonder if Mr Whatsisname is really an angel who disguises his wings beneath a threadbare brown caretaker's coat. But does God want to bless *me*? With all my mixed-up motives, and prayers that send me off to sleep, and my wicked, heartfelt hopes that our minister (he's a "lovely brother", but his sermons are as inspiring as watching paint dry) might be struck by lightning if he preaches on for another minute?

Bless *my* soul? Surely not. We know the truth about ourselves only too well to believe that we might be candidates for blessing – as if there were such a thing as one who is worthy of any divine favour.

Perhaps we think that asking for blessing is superficial and selfish. Let's face it, any personal request could be rejected as trivial, living as we do in a world of screaming need. It does seem the height of absurdity to ask heaven to take notice of my headache/bank balance/housing preferences when there are so many more pressing needs. Unanswered prayer in the affluent West is not a problem – it's answered prayer that creates greater problems.

Yet we serve a Father who chooses to be interested in the tiny lives of his children. Our play, our scuffles, and our fanciful hopes and dreams apparently fascinate him. At the risk of reducing this to sentimentality, there is a Father at the centre of the universe.

And so, while any attempt to reduce prayer to a formula is dangerous, and the Jabez approach could become a superficial mantra, I think that the encouragement to ask for God's smile is basically a good thing. In fact, I'm thinking about writing *The Prayer of Jeffrey.* It too is a simple prayer, but is not based on any obscure Old Testament character – just my own daily experience.

The Prayer of Jeffrey starts like this:

"Heeeeeeeeelpppppp!" Supplicants should note that this intercessory scream is most effective when delivered at a decibel level similar to that of a passing jumbo jet. The more frantic, the better.

Part two goes like this:

"Heeeeeeeeeellllllllllllllllllllpppppppppppp!" Note the longer, more fervent and indeed desperate sentiment expressed in the prayer. Users of *The Prayer of Jeffrey* may alter this according to (a) personal need, (b) mood swing, and (c) housing arrangements. Those already blessed with detached accommodation may feel led to yell a little louder than those in semi-detached accommodation. Flat- and apartment-dwellers might want to skip part two altogether.

Part three is formed in the manner of a question:

"Is anyone up there?" I include this sentence, as this thought tends to surface most times when I pray. Prayer, for me, often gives birth to a sense of absurdity. The ridiculousness of an earnest, one-way conversation snaps at my heels like a puppy, never really hurting me, more a distraction than a menace.

Part four is the gripping conclusion:

"Amen."

OK, I admit it: *my* prayer is not going to sell any books,

be taped onto anyone's fridge, or indeed produce any hot merchandise, but the sentiment is the same as that of *Jabez.* I need God. Desperately. Urgently. I want to know his smile, sense his hand, and hear his voice. So, without apology, I say…

God bless me. And you.

Praying for bread, daily

Most of us are privileged to live in a world of over-stacked supermarket shelves, and so the idea of requesting bread to get us through the day is lost on us. While we should remember that we are in the minority in today's economically unbalanced world, and for many the prayer for some bread daily would be entirely the right request, we can still include ourselves in this prayer. Bread is a symbol of the basic necessities of life. Martin Luther said that "daily bread" was a symbol of everything necessary for the preservation of this life. As he put it, daily bread represented "food, a healthy body, good weather, house, home, wife, children, good government, and peace". It's odd (and telling) that, in compiling his list, Luther put wife and children after good weather…

But for most of us, no angelic delivery service or Elijah and the ravens-type miracle is required in order that our basic needs are met. Why pray for daily bread?

God our security

When we pray about our everyday lives, we are acknowledging that although we work in order to see needs met, ultimately our confidence and sense of security are not placed in us and our ability to earn money, but in God. Stock market crashes, credit crunches, pension crises, banking scandals, and housing market turbulence all point us back to one core source: ultimately God alone can be trusted as provider. That's not to suggest that our labour is not part of the essential provision process, nor indeed that saving and being financially prudent about the future are not entirely appropriate. It's just that we see that God is our acknowledged source, over and above all our best efforts.

This is a healthy prayer, whatever the season of life that we are walking in. When Kay and I returned to the UK after living in the USA for five years, we were facing an uncertain financial future. Having lived comfortably in the USA, we were returning to an annual guarantee of just £3,000 (this was in 1990) and with no confirmed promise of anything else. I can remember the feeling of helplessness that overwhelmed me as we took off in the plane bound for England. What would become of us? We had no house of our own, having sold our home in the USA (with a very small profit, not really enough for a down payment on the house in the UK). Interest rates then were at a hideous level of just over 16 per cent, and we had rented out a flat for an initial period of six months – but then we knew we would have to find somewhere else to live. Property prices were at a booming high.

We *were* able to trust God in that decision, and he did take care of us marvellously. But I notice that every now and again I have a tendency to need to look at the balances of our bank accounts just a little too often, to assure and reassure myself that there is enough. When it comes to what we worship, money alone is the one candidate singled out as the main competition with God (Matthew 6:24). Perhaps it's more of a challenge to ask for bread daily in times of plenty than it is in times of need, but our praying this puts God right at the heart of life: money determines so much about the way that we function.

Nothing mundane in God's eyes

Some early commentators on the Lord's Prayer just couldn't bring themselves to believe that Jesus would "sink" to discussing something as mundane as food. Surely, they reasoned, Jesus was speaking about something deeper, something more "spiritual" than bread for each day? Early church fathers such as Tertullian, Cyprian, and Augustine taught that Jesus was referring not to a hearty loaf but to "the invisible bread of the word of God". Why? Well, surely Jesus is more interested in Bible-reading than toast, they thought. Jerome believed that "daily bread" was a reference to the sacrament of Holy Communion. Thankfully, the Reformers were more down to earth. Calvin argued that to spiritualize the meaning of "daily bread" was "exceedingly absurd".

We too can be guilty of a subtle heresy: that God is only interested in our "spiritual" lives. Many of us persist in the dualistic idea that Bible-reading, prayer, and endless hymn-singing are watched by God with avid interest, but reading a novel, playing a round of golf or anything else "unchurchy" all register far less on the spiritual Richter scale.

A similar error kicks in when we start talking about "secular" work, as if those who work "full time" for the church are doing something *very* useful, but those – most of us – who work in the broader market place are doing something less valuable. The result of this is that we chop our lives up into "sacred" and "secular" boxes and feel schizophrenic as a result. It means that we pray on Sundays for those who teach our children in *Sunday* school, but not for those who teach our children in infant or secondary school five days out of every week. It means that people often demote their work as simply a means to a pay cheque, or an arena for evangelism. John Stott confronts that kind of thinking: "It is very inadequate to see the workplace as having no Christian significance in itself, but only as a well-stocked lake to fish in."

The truth is that work, whatever kind of work it is, is part of the creation plan for us – and not just the result of the fall. We were designed in God's image, and so we were designed to be creative and productive, as he is. God works, and we are called to do likewise. We work as those who are responsible to God as stewards of his resources (Genesis 2:15). And we are commanded by God both to work and to rest – both are acts of worship.

I have come to the conclusion that the only thing that is secular is sin.

Anita Haigh calls us away from building such unbiblical boxes:

> We must reject views of work which define some roles as more 'spiritual' than others. Biblical characters like Joseph the Egyptian Prime Minister, Daniel the Babylonian statesman, Esther the royal mediator, and Paul the preaching tent maker, had a holistic approach where work and worship flowed together. Some are called to serve in the church, others in finance, education, government, etc. All need respect and support. We are all priests and servants of God together.[29]

Pray about your work, or the need for it if you are unemployed. Make your work a prayer. And stop negating the value of it by rejecting it as less than "spiritual".

And praying… daily

I am not in the "I didn't have my daily quiet time today, so God doesn't love me" school. Yet it does seem that the Lord is teaching us that prayer is to be a daily commitment, that every new sunrise brings with it a call to bring that twenty-four-hour segment of our lives under the loving gaze of the interested God.

---

29 "Equipped to Lead" lecture, Sheffield, 1998.

My challenge is that I can live on last week's, last month's, and sometimes last year's faith. When that malaise creeps into my spiritual life, gradual erosion takes place in every area of my life. Sin becomes easier to accommodate. Cynicism springs up like a weed. My Christianity becomes more of a moral code or good idea than a loving friendship. I need Jesus today. There's no such thing as automatic faith, or Christianity on cruise control.

Batteries not included

I was totally exhausted, but had done no real exercise to justify my bone-deep weariness. Instead, my chronic fatigue was the result of jostling with the crowds of fellow turbo-shoppers who were frantically clearing shelves in the New Year sales. The shops were packed from wall to wall with credit card-flashing lemmings seduced by the irresistible beckoning of half-price stuff, desperate to feel the pleasure of purchase now and the pain of payment later. I decided to form an escape committee of one and get out of the madding crowd for just a few minutes. With a sense of relief, I headed into the nearest church – which was also open for business, thankfully – and sat down in a chapel reserved for private prayer. The organist was gloriously practising, and so I began my reflections with some dramatic background music. It was just a little too *Phantom of the Opera*, but certainly gave my praying a hint of drama. The old church smelt reassuringly ancient, the scent of the dust of centuries a welcome change from the clash of warring perfumes in the department store that I'd just escaped.

I scanned the altar, with its beautiful wooden relief: "Lamb of God, grant us thy peace." There were no gold candlesticks; they were locked away, safe from the clutches of any would-be sacred souvenir hunters. The stained-glass window above glowed softly with the fading late afternoon light, the old story told in antique Technicolor. Up there, in intricate glass shards, Christ was suspended on the cross, his friends gazing in medieval open-mouthed admiration. He seemed to look down on me, sad-faced, as I clutched my solitary sale triumph: a purchase of cut-price, bulk-purchase dustbin bags.

My eyes wandered to the candle in a wall-mounted votive glass. It flickered bold and strong in the fading half-light, driving the darkness back, both in the shadows of the nave and in my own dingy heart. And then I noticed the mechanical regularity of the flicker, and the appalling truth dawned upon me: this was not a real candle but a neon host, a Duracell-driven sacrament. No warmth or waxy smoke came from its low-wattage neon design, but just a pre-determined glimmer, a rogue light. It seemed so incongruous, as if someone had grabbed a tiny part of a neon hoarding from Piccadilly Circus and shoved it into this ancient place, like a skyscraper in old Rome.

For a moment I was offended for no rational reason. Somehow the electric host seemed like a cheap trick, an item of ecclesiastical sleight-of-hand. It seemed crass, like a bishop discarding his golden mitre in favour of a "Kiss me quick" hat. I felt the same emptiness that creeps into my soul when a robotic voice apologizes with digital woodenness for yet another late train. Somehow the "We are so sorry for the inconvenience" speech rings hollow when it comes from a heartless machine. For reasons that were probably more sentimental than sacramental, the battery-powered device irritated me. Then logic arrived, and I realized the reason for the hi-tech candle impersonator. I remembered that the days of the priest with little to do were long gone. The amiable round chap, with little more to do than prepare a five-minute sermonette, is no more. The carefree clerics with bicycle clips familiar from thousands of "More tea, vicar?" film and television scenes are now extinct. In their place are a diminishing army of harassed and hurried priests with a brace of parishes to care for, who leap from one morning communion to another like greyhounds.

Of course they don't have time to tend the candle, to pop in every few hours with a genuine wax replacement. The electrical version with a flashing filament is the practical, helpful solution.

Having packed my foolish irritation away, I suddenly found myself staring at the pointed finger of personal challenge. Perhaps my entire faith had become like that ever-ready host: a purposely designed, low-maintenance Christianity, ruggedly created for my busy, frantic existence where time prevents me from being able to tend or care for it.

I'm not gifted at tending things. My office desk looks like the site of the battle of Armageddon, books and papers scattered everywhere in the chaos that I try to pretend I like.

Our garden, if left to my care, would be a useful resource to the Christian church as a missionary-orientation centre for those called to the Amazon. Weeds would flourish in a shocking, choking display, roses would go unpruned, and the grass would reach my shoulders. And my car? I couldn't own a convertible: there would be so much junk in there that the neighbours would think it was a skip (dumpster for my American friends). So many areas of my life suffer from neglect, and they are terribly unkempt as a result.

I am challenged by the fact that Jesus taught that prayer was a daily exercise: evidence of a desire to live out a friendship with God in twenty-four-hour chunks. Living faith, like a living flame, requires nurture, care, and attention: too often mine gets overgrown and derelict.

Ironically, neglect is easier if you belong to a lively, energetic church. You can live off the atmosphere of enthusiasm, plug yourself in to the weekly worship drip-feed, and remain on cruise control in terms of your own personal spirituality. Add to this an annual trek to a large Christian jamboree (and I believe in the value of those events) and you end up with a weekly intravenous experience and an annual event top-up. But hollowness and superficiality lurk within you when Christianity is lived out this way.

A daily note of gratitude to God is evidence of a careful desire to cradle the flame and fuel the fire. Anything truly worthwhile requires inconvenient energy and effort that will disrupt daily hurry, and makes us go out of our way to see something alive develop in our hearts.

Go for authentic, daily faith. Batteries not included.

We, the forgiven, pass forgiveness around

"Forgive us… as we forgive…"

Prayer has become associated with entirely the wrong kinds of people. It is widely regarded as exclusively the habit or hobby of the pious, the saintly, and those worthy of other venerable titles – if indeed such people actually exist outside the Trinity. Good people, we assume, pray. This is a dangerous misapprehension. The Lord's Prayer teaches us that prayer is an activity practised only by sinners. Only those who come with knowledge of their own frailty and incompleteness are welcomed to open their mouths before God. So Jesus has built in an opportunity for us to seek the mercy of God over our sins and our sinfulness when we come close to him. But it seems that, when it comes to the old-fashioned word "sin", we could lurch to one of two extremes.

The paralysis of cringing penitents

Jesus is not calling us into an obsessively introspective wallowing in our sin; rather there is a redemptive chord that is heard loud and clear here – the sweet sound of forgiveness. If we come to pray as overwhelmed, hopelessly smeared deviants who can only list their catalogue of failures, then we are missing the point. While it *is* useful, vital even, to be specific about naming and detailing the sins that we are conscious of, we do not do so simply as a litany of despair, heaping up our transgressions and tipping them over our heads like hot coals. Rather, we come in prayer to find the pardon that we so desperately need – and has been graciously offered. Perhaps it goes without saying, yet we need to be reminded of it: the provision God has made for our pardon has been wrought in great bloodshed and tears at the cross. The just pardon that we are granted because of the shed blood of our wonderful big brother, Jesus, has been the most costly purchase and transaction in history. Having not come cheaply, it should not be refused or squandered. We can come and tip out the wheelbarrows of our foulest mess-ups, our hopelessly mixed-up motives, and break out into the light the most rancid acts of rebellion that have festered in the darkness of secrecy. Dump it all before him, stinking mound that it is.

Failure to understand this will lead us to think that God somehow delights to have us cringe and wince in his presence. One writer, who tragically misunderstood the nature of God, wrote a fearful and yet ridiculous ode to a

God who actually doesn't exist, except in the dark caverns of his own fears and prejudices, a God who is a parody of the evil Marquis de Sade:

> The Marquis de God. Ready to show you how much he cares by punishing you… in a moment of rage, continents convulse with seismic activity. In a fit of moral indignation, he demonstrates the latest craze of viral mutations… The Marquis de God is simply a god who hates. This is a deity who despises sin and sinners with such passion that he'll murder in order to exterminate them. He forces the noblest creation to dance like a trained poodle on the brink of annihilation. Grace, like a dog biscuit, offered or withdrawn, depending on performance.[30]

The writer is completely wrong, not least in the very idea of performance-based grace, "offered or withdrawn like a dog biscuit". Grace is always on offer, and never on the basis of our performance, but on *his*. The performance we offer, in order to find grace, is only in the rebellious act which provoked the need for forgiveness. So when Jesus calls us to ask for forgiveness, he does so that we might simply recognize our need for help. Grace is available – repentance enables us to avail ourselves of it. The call to say, "Forgive us", far from being a call to cringe, is in fact an invitation to get up out of our little mud pools and messes and find the exhilarating pardon of God, who is "my glory, and the lifter of my head" (Psalm 3:3).

---

30 Michael Shevack and Jack Bemporad, *Stupid Ways, Smart Ways to Think About God*, Liguori, MO: Triumph Books, 1993. pp. 17ff.

There is another approach that we are in danger of taking towards our sin, however: far from acknowledging and confessing it, we rationalize and excuse it, and recategorize it as being no sin at all.

Careless fools for sin

In some circles, the very word "sin" offends, as if it were an antique from the past that shouldn't be mentioned in our sophisticated present. We are tempted to rewrite the moral terms and change the price tags of the values of our culture. The lost are not lost, they are "unchurched" or, more hideously, "not yet Christians" (a statement which is stunningly presumptuous about the future intentions of others).

There is a strong temptation, particularly in our post-9/11 culture, to be nervous of anything that smacks of absolutes, and worst still, fundamentalism. While I refuse to line up with the word "fundamentalist", because it implies an approach to the interpretation of Scripture that I am unhappy with, I am equally worried about a relentless pursuit of relevance that causes us to fudge or soft-pedal what is sinful. I hate legalism with every fibre of my being – and yet there is a careless licentiousness that refuses to say any kind of behaviour is abhorrent to God.

Sin is insanity. To be tempted is to be mugged by a temporary madness: an invitation to sip at a momentarily pleasant, then devastatingly poisonous, chalice. Temptation brings with it a temporary but overwhelming amnesia, causing us to forget all we know that is true: about God, about vows and promises that we have made to him and others, about earlier trips into the unsatisfying and shaming trough that is sin, about the advice given and received at the time from a friend. The list of the important truths that we blindly forget could go on. Sin promises liberation, but sets itself to master us and carries its own well-worn handcuffs. How many other people have destroyed their lives, and the lives of others, as they have been duped by its charms?

To ask for forgiveness is to acknowledge the sinfulness of sin. The spell is broken, the con refused, the sleeper wakes up. And then, we have to accept God's response...

Letting Jesus wash you

There is a truth that we must grasp if we are to live in peace with and pray to a holy God – without it we might go mad with torment, the agony of the stained living alongside the utterly pure. The truth is that the only ground that we can stand on, if we are to be close to Jesus, is the ground of grace. The pompous, the self-righteous, and those who would blow their own self-assured trumpets must flee as far as possible from him. Only those who will sit still and let him wash their grotty, grubby feet are allowed to stay around him.

When Jesus surprised his disciples (grace is always a shock) by washing their feet, Peter represented all of us, and indeed the typical human condition as well, by loudly protesting. This was just too good, too kind of Jesus; it was *inappropriate*, or so Peter's mind screamed. But Jesus has always been the utterly "inappropriate" saviour, who will always offend the independence of our so-called human dignity with his outrageous grace. To be so treated is nothing short of a scandal, but here's the point: either Peter accepted the wash cloth and the love that it represented, or he would be able to have no part with Jesus whatsoever. When hearing this, Peter, the typical enthusiast, decided that he would have his whole body washed rather than risk breaking friendship with Jesus. As we pray "Forgive us", we come to One who is armed and ready – with a towel. Receiving the cleansing that we cannot initiate and don't deserve is the only basis upon which we can draw close to him. But this is a cleansing that has little to do with merely private piety. It's a grace that we're called to pass around, as we the forgiven forgive.

Dallas Willard helpfully points out that God does not just offer us grace and mercy – he also offers us *pity*, which, let's face it, offends the very core of our dignity. But this is an important distinction. Pity is not just directed at what we *do*, but is sympathetic to the nature of who we *are*: at best, sheep. When Jesus prayed for his tormentors from the cross, he sought forgiveness for them on the basis of pity: "Father, forgive them, *for they do not know what they are doing*" (Luke 23:34).

> Today, even many Christians read and say,
> 'Forgive us our trespasses' as 'give me a break'...
> this saves the ego and its egotism. 'I am not

> a sinner, I just need a break.' But no! I need more than a break. I need pity because of who I am. If my pride is untouched when I pray for forgiveness, I have not prayed for forgiveness. I don't even know who I am.[31]

As we forgive… graceless spirituality

It's an uncomfortable thought that has nagged me for years, but it persists: "Why is it that some folks who apparently spend lots of time in prayer are so downright nasty?" I've bumped into Christians who allegedly enjoy a splendid prayer life, but they don't seem to remotely resemble the Jesus with whom they spend so much time. Surely, if their praying were effective as well as lengthy, they would manifest some love, some kindness and grace to others, and even a little humour here and there? Why, if they really do spend so much time in the company of the ultimate architect of grace, are they so graceless, so negative, and so addicted to spiritualized snooping and finding fault? Ironically, for some their spirituality has been a toxic force that has affected them for the negative. They are the *worse* for their praying.

Extended prayer is not an automatic guarantee of anything, actually. It didn't produce any positive character transformation in the lives of the Pharisees. Prayer that is *practised* but not *connected* can actually corrupt, giving us a hugely deceptive sense of self-accomplishment. Our supposed "proficiency" in prayer can blind us to huge faults

31 Willard, *The Divine Conspiracy.*

in other areas of our lives. This blindness comes because we view prayer as a profoundly *spiritual* activity, therefore we reason that we must be spiritual because we pray, even if we are a disaster in other areas. But to be proficient in prayer is not necessarily to be proficient at being Christian. Sometimes there are other, more telling indicators.

D. T. Niles told a story of negative piety when he addressed Princeton University:

> Sometime after World War II, during the reconstruction of Europe, the World Council of Churches wanted to see how its money was being spent in some remote parts of the Balkan Peninsula. Accordingly it dispatched John Mackie, who was then the president of the Church of Scotland, and two brothers in the cloth of another denomination – a severe and pietistic denomination – to take a jeep and travel to some of the villages where the funds were being disbursed.
>
> One afternoon Dr. Mackie and the other two clergymen went to call on the Orthodox priest in a small Greek village. The priest was overjoyed to see them, and was eager to pay his respects. Immediately, he produced a box of Havana cigars, a great treasure in those days, and offered each of his guests a cigar. Dr. Mackie took one; bit the end off, lit it, puffed a few puffs, and said how good it was. The other gentlemen looked horrified and said, "No, thank you, we don't smoke."
>
> Realising he had somehow offended the two who refused, the priest was anxious to make

> amends. So he excused himself and reappeared in a few minutes with a flagon of his choicest wine. Dr. Mackie took a glassful, sniffed it like a connoisseur, sipped it and praised its quality. Soon he asked for another glass. His companions, however, drew themselves back even more noticeably than before and said, "No, thank you, we don't drink!"
>
> Later, when the three men were in the jeep again, making their way up the rough road out of the village, the two pious clergymen turned upon Dr. Mackie with a vengeance. "Dr. Mackie," they insisted, "do you mean to tell us that you are the president of the Church of Scotland and an officer of the World Council of Churches and you smoke and drink?"
>
> Dr. Mackie had had all he could take, and his Scottish temper got the better of him. "No, dammit, I don't,' he said, 'but somebody had to be a Christian."[32]

Piety, if it is not truly Jesus-centred, can poison.

An irony: spirituality itself is heady, dangerous stuff

The poisoned chalice of pride is often offered to those who are more recognized for their praying. In recent years, it's become usual to describe a group of people with a special gifting in prayer as *intercessors.* At one level, it's reasonable to

32 Quoted by John Killinger in Pulpit Digest, July/August, 1992, pp. 12-13.

recognize and release people into the gift and call that God gives. But, on the other hand, I'm a little nervous of this tagging of people. The "intercessors" can begin to act like the Royal Marines of prayer, the crack troops of spiritual warfare, all-weather warriors who can penetrate areas of darkness hitherto unexplored by humankind.

Sometimes the intercessory gift is genuine – but gets hijacked. I can think of a church right now where the intercessors are causing all kinds of grief, demanding to know details of just who in the church is going through marriage problems, where there are struggles with teenagers – because they alone have the keys for breakthrough in these areas of difficulty. A critical attitude can easily settle on the landing strip of the intercessor. Because they have a genuine radar perception, God shares "intelligence" information with them on a real "need to know" basis. But if that intelligence is not used solely as fuel for prayer, a critical attitude is waiting to envelop them.

I remember seeing this in action when living in a small community in southern Oregon, USA. A number of the men in the church had developed a burden for prayer that was authentic and committed. They were gathering together at 4 a.m. every day at the church building. Sounds good? It was – for a while. But here's how the "lead intercessor" announced the meetings over a series of Sunday mornings:

Week one: the leader of the prayer group walks quietly to the pulpit, a broad, excited grin on his face, his eyes sparkling with real joy.

"A few of us are feeling that God is asking us to pray

every day for this community. We've had a wonderful week as we've got together each morning, and I'd like to invite you all to come and be a part of it. We meet at 4 a.m. in the prayer room – hope to see you there."

Week two: the same leader, his face now wreathed in a weaker smile, and his shoulders slightly hunched from sheer tiredness, walks slowly to the pulpit.

His voice has a weary drone. "This week, a few people who are responding faithfully to a call to sacrificial prayer have been braving the early morning cold to come out and pray for this community that is lost and in great darkness. We could use your help too. Hope to see you tomorrow morning at 4 a.m."

Week three: slowly the same prayer leader, close to total exhaustion now, blinks wearily at the congregation. There is no smile now, and his eyes are slightly glazed. Tinges of blue can be seen in the bags beneath those eyes. He is annoyed.

"Yet again, the needs of this community are being borne upon the shoulders of a remnant of this church, a small but mighty group, who are sick to death of insipid, lukewarm Christianity and who are valiantly continuing the spiritual warfare that is needed if this wretched community is to be saved. Are there others here who will reject the kind of half-heartedness that makes Jesus vomit? See you tomorrow, I hope."

Week four: (the last week that *the few* gathered): the prayer leader now looks like Lazarus – before Jesus passed by. He can barely string two sentences together, and he is enraged with the white-hot-poker passion of the incensed zealot. His eyelids droop their testimony to his state of sleep deprivation, but they shroud eyes that are ablaze with anger. His voice trembles as he speaks, barely able to contain his incensed indignation.

"Does anyone around here really care at all? Does anyone really believe the Bibles that we hold in our hands today? God will surely judge the pathetic lukewarm hearts of all of us."

He looks around the building with a suddenly alert, piercing gaze, searching out non-praying people for a lightning bolt. He continues, his voice slowly and methodically passing sentence, like a judge with black cap passing down the sentence of the hangman's noose: "This will be our last week of special prayer. Come and join us if you can be bothered... and may the Lord have mercy upon your souls."

Not many people turned out to pray that week. The otherwise nice chap had been turned into a gibbering religious ranter. The sad epilogue to the story is that his marriage later broke up, and, as far as I know, neither he nor his former wife has anything to do with God these days. The passionate pursuit of God has been tragically hijacked by cynicism and disappointment. Of course, extended prayer is a discipline that is vital – but beware the hijacking of even the purest forms of spiritual aspiration.

Ready to forgive: help, there are humans around here…

We are called to move in the direction of forgiving as part of the attitude of prayer, and it can feel like an Everest to climb. Our struggle to forgive is sometimes rooted in the surprise that we feel that we might actually have to. We can develop a completely unrealistic set of expectations, particularly when it comes to our churches (we touched on this earlier). Someone came to me recently and announced in hushed and stunned whispers that they had discovered that their church had some weaknesses. One would think that this would come as no surprise, and that to reach this obvious conclusion was not exactly rocket science, but we can forget that we are ourselves basically human. We are prone to sin, mistakes, false motives, loud mouths, impurity, thoughtlessness, and a host of other maladies associated with the human condition. And, in the church, we are still hemmed in by… humans, like ourselves. But we want to forget this, and live in a Utopia where all is sweetness and light. Beware: disappointment is just around the corner.

I occasionally encounter this "He's more than human, you know" attitude when I turn up as a guest speaker at a church service. The prayer time beforehand can be utterly terrifying. Genuinely kind people gather around me, massage my shoulders, shout in my ear and spit in my face, and ask the Lord to heal the sick, cast out demons, and raise the dead, during the service and through little *me*, the hapless guest speaker.

And I'm not alone in being elevated to superhuman status: people often do this to church leaders generally. If they make a mistake, take a wrong turn, or change the service time (usually a dangerous decision) and the numbers go down by six as a result of it, then look out... there are always those whose quick response to any kind of error from leadership, no matter how small, is to condemn.

The command of Jesus is clear: we've been shown much, much grace. So let's pass it around, lest – to paraphrase that little story about the unjust servant – we who have been forgiven a lottery-sized list of transgressions take up accountancy and meticulously audit everybody else's overdrafts.

Grace requires compromise

We Christians can be people of such principle that we don't know when to relax, and end up majoring on minors. When that happens, grace is always the first casualty. "Here I stand, I can do no other," we cry, Martin Luther-style, in the bold spirit of the Reformation, as we protest about the proposal to change the hymnbooks, or, God forbid, move the piano from the left side of the church to the right side. And worse still, we name God in our protests, insisting that he is as aggrieved as we are. Of course, deep down we know the truth: God doesn't care where the piano is sited. Pack away the prayer meeting and stop fasting about *that* decision. The difficulty is further compounded by our insistence on using spiritual language in our conflicts. We don't say, "I don't like you." No, our Christian code causes us to cry, "You have grieved my spirit." What?

The use of the word "compromise" in the above heading may shock some, and I have chosen it deliberately. Jesus compromised all the time in his daily walk with his friends and disciples. Couldn't he have spent all day, every day, listing their faults and weaknesses? But he did not. And he wrote to two of the seven churches of Revelation 1–3 and found no fault with them whatsoever. Does that mean that they were flawless, without any hint of weakness? Of course not, but it does mean that while Jesus is perfect, he isn't picky, crusading about every single issue of weakness and jumping on every mistake. What an irony: those who have been showered with amazing grace, running around with magnifying glasses in search of sin, desperately hunting down and exposing everybody else's shortcomings.

Misunderstandings about forgiveness

In praying about forgiving others, we are not merely stating an intention or vowing to forgive: we are asking for help in what is often a very difficult act. People are damaged when they are rushed into forgiveness, as if forgiving were a casual act. The abused can be made to think they are guilty because of the right anger that they feel; this is a new abuse. A Christian psychologist friend tells me that he often sees people who have been damaged by what he calls premature forgiveness.

Indeed, we Christians don't do well with anger. We're nervous of it, because it isn't tidy or nice. But a woman who has been raped has every right to feel very angry, and a quick prayer renouncing those agonizing emotions will not fix everything. Indeed, it may cause further damage.

Forgiveness is not an act that seeks to pretend that what was done to us was not wrong. On the contrary, the very fact that *forgiveness* is offered is a clear recognition that sin has indeed been committed. If it wasn't wrong, it does not need to be forgiven. Forgiveness does not bless sin. Nor does forgiveness release the other party from the negative consequences of their actions. Everything may not return as it was; some relationships may be fractured beyond repair. Forgiveness does not imply that there will actually be full reconciliation. The damage done to a marriage shattered by adultery may be an example. The aggrieved party may indeed forgive, but that does not necessarily mean that the marriage will continue. Scripture seems to give the wounded party a choice. In just the same way that we can be forgiven by God for our follies, yet may still suffer the natural consequences of them, so forgiveness doesn't cancel out the effect that our sin has created.

Surely forgiveness has little to do with feelings; again, it may be that our emotions are screaming with indignation and itching for vengeance. Forgiveness is a choice that says that I will end my self-appointed role as the avenger.

Instead, I will, by God's help, hand the situation and the person over to God.

Forgiveness and prayer

Bitterness is a consuming force, fuelled by obsession. It can fill our waking moments and our dreams at night. It makes the possibility of a single-minded pursuit of God in prayer unlikely, as it robs me of my energy and clutters my heart and brain with dark, vain, and impotent thoughts. It will destroy my ability to pray for others. Bitterness is not a targeted, specific emotion but a clumsy, omni-directional force that spills over and sours all our relationships. We can hardly pray that the kingdom will come in the world when our own hearts are wrestling to be the god of justice – or more likely, injustice – in our own theatres of relational war. And our wrestling goes on and on, and causes untold damage – particularly in the church, which is why the writer to the Hebrews was adamant in saying: "See to it that no one misses the grace of God and that no bitter root grows up to cause trouble and defile many" (Hebrews 12:15).

Myra Hindley was the other half of one of the most infamous and hated couples of modern criminal history. Together with her lover Ian Brady, Hindley subjected young children to unspeakable sexual abuse and torture before killing them in what became known as the Moors Murders. The British public was outraged when, at their trial, a recording made of one of the young victims by this evil pair was played. The distraught parents in the public gallery had to listen to the haunting sounds of their beloved child sobbing, begging for mercy, and pleading for Mum. The nation felt a fury that has raged and blazed unabated since.

The fire still burns. Hindley died some years ago in prison; the police were forced to mount a special guard on her body lest, even in death, she become the target for vengeance, a vengeance that she was obviously beyond. And the sadness is that more lives have been lost since those innocent children died in the bleak night on the moors long ago. Parents and relatives have spent their whole lives on a journey of unrequited hatred, a further tragic waste, a never-ending hunt for a payback that never really came. Even if they had been able to get their hands around the necks of this terrible pair, it would not have brought satisfaction.

I shrink back from what I have just written, as I know nothing of the awful, gut-wrenching pain and loss that they felt. No wonder forgiveness, whatever it pardons, can only come as a result of heaven's help. But I can point to one who has been to a similar hell – and back.

Imagine this scene from a courtroom trial in South Africa:

> A frail black woman stands slowly to her feet. She is something over 70 years of age. Facing her from across the room are several white security police officers, one of whom, Mr. van der Broek, has just been tried and found implicated in the murders of both the woman's son and her husband some years before.

It was indeed Mr. van der Broek, it has now been established, who had come to the woman's home a number of years back, taken her son, shot him at point-blank range, and then burned the young man's body on a fire while he and his officers partied nearby.

Several years later, van der Broek and his cohorts had returned to take away her husband as well. For many months she heard nothing of his whereabouts. Then, almost two years after her husband's disappearance, van der Broek came back to fetch the woman herself. How vividly she remembers that evening, going to a place beside a river where she was shown her husband, bound and beaten, but still strong in spirit, lying on a pile of wood. The last words she heard from his lips as the officers poured gasoline over his body and set him aflame were, "Father, forgive them."

And now the woman stands in the courtroom and listens to the confessions offered by Mr. van der Broek. A member of South Africa's Truth and Reconciliation Commission turns to her and asks, "So what do you want? How should justice be done to this man who has so brutally destroyed your family?"

"I want three things," begins the old woman, calmly, but confidently. "I want first to be taken to the place where my husband's body was burned so that I can gather up the dust and give his remains a decent burial."

She pauses, then continues, "My husband and son were my only family. I want, secondly, therefore, for Mr. van der Broek to become my son. I would like for him to come twice a month to the ghetto and spend a day with me so that I can pour out on him whatever love I still have remaining within me.

"And finally," she says, "I want a third thing. I would like Mr. van der Broek to know that I offer him my forgiveness because Jesus Christ died to forgive. This was also the wish of my husband. And so, I would kindly ask someone to come to my side and lead me across this courtroom so that I can take Mr van der Broek in my arms, embrace him, and let him know that he is truly forgiven."

As the court assistants come to lead the elderly woman across the room, Mr. van der Broek, overwhelmed by what he has just heard, faints. And, as he does, those in the courtroom, friends, family, neighbours – all victims of decades of oppression and injustice – begin to sing, softly, but assuredly, "Amazing grace, how sweet the sound, that saved a wretch like me."[33]

Grace at the heart of it all

Perhaps day-to-day forgiveness is fuelled by the knowledge that not only are we all human, but as Christians, we are part of the community of the condemned-but-now-pardoned. Charles Colson tells of visiting a prison, in the Brazilian

33 James Krabill, in *Keep the Faith, Share the Peace*, newsletter of the Mennonite Church Peace and Justice Committee, vol. 5, No. 3, June 1999.

city of São José dos Campos, that was turned over to two Christians twenty years ago:

> They called it Humaita, and their plan was to run it on Christian principles. The prison has only two full-time staff; the rest of the work is done by inmates. Every prisoner is assigned another inmate to whom he is accountable. In addition, every prisoner is assigned a volunteer family from the outside that works with him during his term and after his release. Every prisoner joins a chapel program, or else takes a course in character formation.
>
> When I visited Humaita, I found the inmates smiling – particularly the murderer who held the keys, opened the gates, and let me in. Wherever I walked I saw men at peace. I saw clean living areas, people working industriously. The walls were decorated with biblical sayings from Psalms and Proverbs. Humaita has an astonishing record. Its recidivism rate is 4 percent compared to 75 percent in the rest of Brazil and the United States. How is all this possible?
>
> I saw the answer when my guide escorted me to the notorious punishment cell once used for torture. Today, he told me, that block houses only a single inmate. As we reached the end of a long concrete corridor and he put the key into the lock, he paused and asked, 'Are you sure you want to go in?'
>
> 'Of course,' I replied impatiently. 'I've been in isolation cells all over the world.' Slowly he swung

open the massive door, and I saw the prisoner in that punishment cell: a crucifix, beautifully carved by the Humaita inmates – the prisoner Jesus hanging on the cross.

'He's doing time for all the rest of us,' my guide said softly.[34]

---

34 Quoted in Donald W. Mccullough, *The Trivialization of God*, Nav. Press, 1995, pp. 95-96

Come to God, whatever the season

"Lead us not into temptation, but deliver us from evil."

Troubles come...

A story is told of a policeman who was seeking promotion to Sergeant, and so was taking a test paper. In the course of the examination he found a question focused on decision-making and ordering priorities. And the question read:

"You are driving along a road in your patrol car, when suddenly a car coming from the other direction veers across the road and smashes into another car. As you approach the first car, you notice the wife of the police inspector who is in charge of your station is driving it, and that a very strong smell of alcohol is coming from her car. You look into the *other* car, and notice that a well-known local criminal and thief, who has jumped bail and is on the run, is driving that car, and he is sitting there looking dazed. In the back of his car are boxes of video recorders. Just then a tanker, trying to avoid the two cars, veers off the road and ploughs into some shop fronts. The tanker driver, distraught, jumps out of the cab and comes running towards you, yelling, 'Fire! Fire! *Do* something, officer!', and then you notice that the words 'Toxic waste – High explosive' are marked on the side of the tanker. Just then a gang of twenty-five large chaps who just happened to be passing begin looting the shop, which has now caught fire. *Please list your priorities and decisions.*"

The policeman taking the test paper gave this precise answer: "Priority and decision number 1: remove uniform and mingle with crowd."

I'm with him. I don't like trouble, and used to feel bad about that because I thought that I was supposed to greet trial and difficulty with a sense of breathless, thrilled excitement.

> Oh, deep and prevailing joy... I have the flu today, my ears are so bunged up that I feel like I'm twenty fathoms beneath water, my nose is dripping like a tap in need of a washer, and I have the inestimable privilege of walking through my day with two large menthol inhalers stuck up my nostrils. What blessedness is this? How shall my faith grow as a result, I wonder?

Scripture seems to instruct us to be glad *in* trials, because with God, nothing is wasted. His grace is mine, his presence is sure, and he has the knack of bringing something good out of something bad, like a stronger faith. But that doesn't mean that I've got to pretend that I like it or wander down the street just hoping that I'll trip up and break my nose, just the thing to help refine my ability to rejoice in tribulation. When it comes to bad stuff happening to good people (or even me), I want to join the aforementioned constable: remove uniform and mingle with crowd – in other words, get away from the source of hassle as quickly as possible.

I like bright, sunny, balmy days, filled with laughter, friendship, love, and good wine. Sadly, we are not promised only days of this sort – indeed the opposite. Jesus did actually promise us that we would have trouble in this world – not my favourite text, and certainly not one that I've got stuck to my refrigerator door.

And here we are taught to pray about temptation and evil – which is not primarily about temptation to sin, although that's part of it. More specifically, it is a prayer that we might not face trials of many kinds. But before we think about this in relationship to prayer, let's face the unpalatable fact – suffering *will* touch us all in some way in this life. It is unavoidable. No amount of pretending, super-faith, or ultra-triumphal talk will change that.

A little chat about suffering

Nowhere does Scripture suggest that Christians will experience freedom from suffering – on the contrary, the Bible makes it very clear that suffering and trials are a very likely part of the life of faith.

Check out the lives of the New Testament Christians and you'll see that pain was very much part of their daily experience. Our long-suffering ancestors tasted *tribulation* – the Greek word means pressure, and in classical Greek it is always used in its literal sense. It is used, for instance, to describe the plight of a man who was tortured to death by being slowly crushed by a great boulder laid upon his chest. Some of my readers know that feeling right now, even as you turn this page: the rock that you carry of that sickness, that anxious fear for your wayward prodigal, that financial burden that just won't go away... The rock sits on your chest, threatening at times to crush the very life out of you. When I first wrote this, I was walking through a period of my life when I knew the weight of a rock that was crushing me for a year or so. Some days that rock eclipsed my view of God – I could barely squint around it to get any view of him at all. And at other times, the weight of it made me breathless and tempted me to feel that I couldn't do anything at all useful – I had neither the faith nor the energy.

As well as tribulation, the early Christians suffered *poverty*, and in many cases were described as being destitute, having nothing of worth to call their own. Generally speaking, the early Christians were poor. They not only had to bear the obvious burden of caring for their family and themselves, but also experienced the huge social stigma that was attached to having little. Roman thinking suggested that to be poor meant that you were of absolutely no consequence. The poverty of the Christians may have stemmed from a combination of their background before they came to Christ and the hardship they suffered after their conversion, perhaps because some of their homes were plundered.

And then, if all this were not bad enough, the early Christians were slandered and maligned, and accused of the most appalling crimes. Perfectly innocent ideas, such as the brotherhood and sisterhood of believers and the Eucharist, were twisted and made to sound as if incest and cannibalism were common practice among the "Nazarenes". Talk of loving one's "brother or sister" and of eating Christ's body and drinking his blood was used to fuel the slander.

The early Christians recognized the inevitability of their suffering. As Christ suffered, so would they. Continuing his mission, they would incur tribulation because the world hates the disciples as much as it did their Lord. Suffering for his sake was counted as a privilege. New Testament writers saw that trials were to be endured patiently rather than rebelliously, because God was working his purpose out in his children's lives.

They certainly testified to the reality that none of us wants to admit: often those who have walked the hardest pathway are the most gracious and mature in their faith, because faith can grow stronger through trials. In the darker days, we are driven back to the truth that we will share Christ's ultimate triumph, the foretaste of which is our experience of small, daily victories. Therefore, sufferings give birth to hope in us, and give us a glimpse of the eternal horizon – no present suffering, the Bible teaches, compares with the rewards that await the faithful follower of Christ.

And so... we will suffer.

Yet prayer still asks for us to be delivered from trials...

Why don't we want trials? Mainly, I suggest, because we don't trust our ability to cope with them well. Faith can indeed become like gold in the furnace of trial, but that doesn't mean that I have to like the furnace.

Jesus was once assailed by a couple of his friends (who had brought their mother along for added weight), who asked to be given special thrones of honour. In responding, he asked them whether they would be able to "drink the cup" that he was going to drink – the cup of suffering, typified by the Gethsemane experience. They, full of a groundless but heady self-confidence, responded that they were ready for the cup – a ludicrous assertion in retrospect, considering that when Calvary day finally rolled up, they all ran away.

James and John *would* one day sip from suffering's unwelcome cup – one day John would be exiled in Patmos, and James would be martyred on a whim by Herod. But in the meantime, they forgot their own fragility. Peter also overestimated his own capacity for trial, asserting he would never deny Christ, even if everybody else did. I think that I can happily pray that I might be spared days of trial, if at all possible. I think I can trust God for them, but I just don't trust *me*.

… and prayer is devil-aware

Trials aren't sin – but the time of trial is often the time when we are tempted to sin. Satan would tempt believers to be defeated in their seasons of suffering. Obviously, God does not "lead us" into temptation – God cannot tempt us with evil, so there is no need for us to ask him not to when his word assures us that he won't! John Stott believed the best translation of this phrase is "Deliver us from the evil one", who of course is the tempter. The time of trial is often the time when the enemy would seek to establish a foothold in our lives, perhaps sowing seeds of bitterness and disappointment towards God.

We must pray for a balanced view of Satan. There are some who see the "hand of the enemy" in every tiny calamity, many of which are the result of our negligence. Yet others are loath to see life as any kind of battlefield at all, fearing an unhealthy preoccupation with the devil. As they do so, they miss the message of the last book of the Bible: behind the scenes, in the macro and the micro, a battle rages between good and evil.

The God who knows the dark days

As we come to the Father, "in the heavens", we remind ourselves that we come to the God who not only knows our dark days but shares in our suffering. At the heart of Christianity is the cross: the symbol that forever reminds us that God has entered a suffering world, to suffer for us and with us. It is not a cliché, but a historical reality that, however deep our pain, he's been there, and is there with us now.

Of course, in affirming that the cross demonstrates that Christ has walked through pain and therefore he knows what it us to walk with us in ours, we never lose sight of the truth that this is not just about identification. Just before Jesus died, he turned to the criminal at his side and *did not* say, "I tell you the truth, today I am with you at Calvary" – that's empathy – but he *did say*, "I tell you the truth, today you will be with me in paradise."

God does not just weep with us, but – through the work of the cross – is able to bring his power as well as his tears to our situation. Jesus is not just our sympathetic friend, he is our sympathetic high priest. And the cross is far more than a love letter made of wood.

In dark days, we pray and remind ourselves that darkness does not mean that we have been deserted. In the library of Corpus Christi College, Cambridge, is a grubby Bible which belonged to Thomas Bilney, one of the minor characters of the English Reformation in the sixteenth century. He was no great hero and sometimes wavered in his faith. But in the end he was burnt at the stake for his commitment to the gospel. In his Bible, the verse which comforted him in his last days (in his version, in Latin) is heavily marked in ink: "Fear not, for I have redeemed you; I have summoned you by name; you are mine... When you walk through the fire, you will not be burned; the flames will not set you ablaze For I am the Lord, your God, the Holy One of Israel, your Saviour" (Isaiah 43:1–3).

We can be quick to assume that the advent of pain and suffering in our lives suggests that God has become distant or perhaps has even deserted us completely, abandoning us to our "fate". But although God is not the author of our pain, he is fully aware of all that we face. We must remember this when we face pain or opposition.

I have not been as well equipped for dark days as I might, because I have not sufficiently valued and sought out the prayer support of others. Make it a practice to find out how you can pray for your friends and others – and let them know how they can pray for you. Don't hesitate. The Bible places a high value on our praying for those who suffer: "Remember those in prison as if you were their fellow prisoners, and those who are mistreated as if you yourselves were suffering" (Hebrews 13:3) and "Carry each other's burdens, and in this way you will fulfil the law of Christ" (Galatians 6:2).

And pray for endurance – an oft-mentioned New Testament theme. As Stephen Travis says, "Remember that, for most of us, the Christian life is a marathon race, not a sprint. There is no quick escape from hardship. There is what has been called 'a long obedience in the same direction'."[35]

Being honest in prayer: let me tell you about what it's like, God

I have had some wonderful times of prayer, which involved me telling God very clearly that I didn't like what was going on. I see absolutely no merit in pretending or speechmaking. God knows what's in our hearts anyway, and he is able to cope with our protests. We make them in the knowledge that God is God, and therefore worthy of our respect and submission. We do so knowing that we are looking at life from our vantage point, which is a billion miles below his – yet still we can be authentic. When Jesus cried, "My God, my God, why have you forsaken me?", he was doing more than reading a prophetic script (the Messiah is supposed to quote Old Testament Scriptures shortly before dying, so here we go: "My God..."). Rather, he was sobbing out the agony of what he really felt at that moment – *and* fulfilling the oracles of old in being the rejected one. The most common prayers of the psalmists are "Why?" and "How long?" We can join in the litany of reality too.

---

35 Travis, *You've Got Mail*, p. 34.

Back to "Father" again – affirming our identity on the dark days

We tend to think of the agony of Calvary as being mainly about physical and spiritual pain, but I suggest that Jesus was being tormented emotionally in a way that focused on who he was in his Sonship. Think about it: as he hangs there he is at his lowest ebb, doing his greatest work – and the taunting voices shout a familiar question, cheer-led from hell: "Who are you, Jesus?" Our spiritual identity is critical. Satan would wrest it from our grasp with the whisper, "Who do you think you are?", which is why God shouts louder about identity in Scripture:

> But you are a chosen people, a royal priesthood, a holy nation, a people belonging to God, that you may declare the praises of him who called you out of darkness into his wonderful light. Once you were not a people, but now you are the people of God; once you had not received mercy, but now you have received mercy. (1 Peter 2:9–10)

These are not rosy platitudes from a banal-greeting-card God, nor poetic sentimentality; they form the backbone of who we are in Christ. Luke 23:35–39 describes three moments at the cross when the cry went up in the face of Jesus himself: who do you think you are?

The rulers sneered: "He saved others; let him save himself *if he is* the Christ of God, the Chosen One."

The soldiers mocked: "They offered him wine vinegar and said, '*If you are* the king of the Jews, save yourself.'"

And then one of the criminals who hung there "hurled insults at him": "*Aren't you the Christ?* Save yourself and us!"

All three are singing from the same satanic song sheet – an attack on the jugular of Christ's identity. Of course, this is actually just a repeat performance: it had been played before at the beginning of Jesus' ministry, as he was tempted in the wilderness. Again, it was three times there that Satan hissed, "If you are the Son of God…" And so, at the beginning of Christ's earthly ministry, Satan sought to undermine his identity, which had been so beautifully affirmed by the Father at his baptism, when the voice declared, "You are my Son, whom I love" (Luke 3:22).

Watch a principle at work. In Luke 3, the Father affirms the identity of Jesus. In Luke 4, Satan questions it. And then, at the *end* of his earthly ministry, affirmation and questioning takes place again. In his twenty-second chapter, Luke alone records that an angel comforted Jesus in the garden of Gethsemane. And then the various parasites gather at the cross, ready to suck the very life of Jesus out of him as they lay siege to his identity, three times again. But he will not be so mugged. Twice he yells out the family name: "Father!"

"Father, forgive them, for they do not know what they are doing" (Luke 23:34).

"Father, into your hands I commit my spirit" (Luke 23:46).

Dark days conspire to make us lose sight of who we are: to forget that we belong to God as his beloved children. Sometimes, the only prayer you can muster when the grey skies gather is the sob, "Father". It is enough. It says, "I am yours. I belong to you. My trial has not obscured the truth of who I am. Whatever I have lost, this I will not lose. I am yours. You are mine."

Look up on the dark days

I've heard it said that too much preaching about eternity and heaven produces Christians who are "too heavenly minded to be of any earthly use" – a phrase I've used myself. But I wonder: has the pendulum swung yet again, causing us to lose sight of the incredible future before us? Contemplating the trials of this life in the context of eternity, the New Testament writers were able to see them as "momentary" (2 Corinthians 4:17), as part of a life that is "a mist that appears for a little while and then vanishes" (James 4:14). Christ's coming will be in "just a very little while" (Hebrews 10:37). Paul struggled with a genuine dilemma between remaining on earth to continue his ministry or departing to be with Christ for ever (Philippians 1:21–24). Eternity loomed large in the thinking of the early Christians.

> Sometimes, all you have is the future. And it is hope that takes you through. There was much of this in the life and death of Jesus, who "for the joy set before him endured the cross, scorning

its shame, and sat down at the right hand of the throne of God" (Hebrews 12:2).

One day the half-sight of prayer will be over. Our struggling to peer through the fog will end, banished by the clear sunrise of his appearing. Prayer, as we have known it, will be abandoned, an out-of-date apparatus that saw us through the mists but will be unnecessary now that we are fully at home with the Father.

And so... "We will be with the Lord for ever. Therefore encourage each other with these words" (1 Thessalonians 4:17-18).

In the meantime, we often find ourselves in the swirling mists.

When I was concluding the first edition of this book, some years ago, I suddenly found myself in yet another fog. Back then, banner headlines screamed the tragic news that policeman Stephen Oake, a forty-year-old father of three from Manchester, had been stabbed to death by some suspected terrorists. Stephen, a much beloved and respected Christian, was a member of Poynton Baptist Church. I was speaking at the Mainstream Conference, a gathering of around 400 Baptists, when the news came through. Kay and I have a great love for the Poynton crowd, some of whom were there at the conference. We were due to leave at 10 p.m. to drive to Heathrow to stay overnight and then board a plane for America. But, perhaps madly, we lingered with a few of the Poynton people, wanting to savour our final moments of laughter and fun with these warm, animated lovers of God.

We knew that we wouldn't get to the airport until 2 a.m., but these people were worth the late-night drive. I'm glad we stayed.

We were just about to say our goodbyes when our friend Mark Elder came into the room. His announcement, made through eyes clouded with tears, stopped us in our tracks, as he told us that dear Stephen was the victim of murder. Waves of shock rippled around the room, and for a moment Kay and I felt that perhaps we should not be there at this time, intruders on their grief. And then, after the briefest moment, one by one, we just began to sob out prayers to God. Desperate, urgent, inarticulate, emergency prayers; stumbling intercessions for Stephen's family, now brutally robbed of a husband and father; heartfelt requests for wisdom for Rob and Marion White, the leaders of the church, as they were on their way back, even then, to try to minister and bring comfort in this darkest of nights. One or two prayers never ended with a formal *Amen*: the tears were their signal of conclusion. Looking back, I see that we were in a profound moment of kingdom reality that night. An evening of laughter and fun, wine and stories, was suddenly mingled with tears and anguish and questioning and heartbreak. The kingdom here, touching our lives with the vintage wine of friendship and reality, yet placed in a real world where the enemy of us all still is rampaging in his killing, stealing, destroying missions. Sometimes we raise our glasses in the midst of tears and confusion.

Light lives in the midst of darkness; the gold of heaven's king nestles in the dirt of a messed-up, bloody world. The future is bright – yet we live in the *meantime*. So, in that meantime, keep breathing all your prayers. Shout the urgent ones. Whisper your worship. Keep pressing in – and remember, prayer is for the fallen ones, like me, like you.

Thanks for taking this brief journey with me. Can we pray together before you go?

Join me in this paraphrase of the prayer of Clement of Rome, a contemporary of John the Apostle, who finally did get to drink deeply of the cup of suffering and discovered that God was with him on Patmos, the isle of exile, and was his strength and source on the darkest day.

Open our inward eyes to recognize you, even though you are the highest in high heaven, the Holy One among the ranks of all the holy.

You, Lord God, bring down the proud and outwit the cunning.

You promote the humble and make the arrogant fall.

You hold in your hand every issue of life: whether we are to be poor or rich, whether we are to live or to die.

You see every spirit, good or evil, and read the inmost thoughts and intentions of every heart.

When we are in danger, you come to our aid.

When we are feeling desperate, you save us from our sense of failure.

When events in the world overshadow us, help us to remember who you are: the Creator and Overseer of every living being.

Amen.[36]

And… may God bless you.

36 Adapted from David Winter, *After the Gospels*, Oxford: BRF, 2001

By the same author

Rediscovering the Father Heart of God

Friends of God (with Cleland Thom)

Walking Backwards

Elijah, Anointed and Stressed, later published as *Going Public*

Lucas on Life

Lucas on Life 2

How Not to Pray

Grace Choices

Gideon: Power from Weakness

Lucas Out Loud

Will Your Prodigal Come Home?

Creating a Prodigal-Friendly Church

Helen Sloane's Diary

Up Close and Personal: What Helen Did Next

Lucas Unleashed

Life with Lucas

Life with Lucas 2

Life with Lucas 3

Seriously Funny (with Adrian Plass)

Seriously Funny 2 (with Adrian Plass)

There are No Strong People

I Was Just Wandering

Things My Grandchildren Taught Me